Circumstantial Evidence

Circumstantial Evidence

John Penter

FARADAY PRESS / SAN FRANCISCO / 1981

82070110

Copyright © 1981 by Faraday Press

First Edition
First Printing

Library of Congress Catalog Card Number: 81-67265

ISBN 0-939762-00-5

Printed in the U.S.A.

Contents

Circumstantial Evidence

1
The Origin

I bent down, looking over the edge of the trench. "Excuse me, are you the Archaeologist?"

A head of gray hair became visible and surprised, bespectacled eyes looked at me. "No, I'm the Historian."

"My name is Penter, John Penter. I sent a letter . . . "

"Oh, yes. You're the chap who's interested in the sources of the Old Testament."

A second man appeared, younger than the first, holding a clay fragment and a brush. "Who are you?"

"My name is Penter. I wrote to you . . . "

"Ah, yes, I remember now. I am not sure we can help you, though. You seem to be asking questions for which we have no definite answers yet."

"Well, I'm sure you can tell me more than I know so far."

The Archaeologist scratched his face, the grime from his fingers smudging his cheeks. "Always happy to help if we can."

The two climbed out of the dig.

"Let me come straight to the heart of the matter," I said. "How far back in time does our knowledge of religion go?"

The Archaeologist nodded to the Historian.

"Well," the Historian answered hesitatingly, "as far as you want to. The problem is that, the further back we go the more uncertain our knowledge becomes. You see, there were already elaborate religious beliefs and rituals long before the advent of writing."

We began walking toward the nearby inn. "I realize that," I said, "but, putting all the known facts together, what can we say today about the earliest forms of religion?"

"We can assume today with a fair degree of certainty that the early religions of man stemmed from fear. Science as we know it today did not exist 10,000 years ago, not even a primitive one. There was no explanation for most of the phenomena that man was exposed to. He could not explain lightning, thunder, earthquakes, floods, high winds, or fire. So man made up an explanation: spirits. Spirits caused everything. Good spirits were in the beneficial phenomena such as the sun, the moon, the planets, trees, or majestic mountains. Bad spirits were in the frightening and harmful occurrences such as lightning or darkness.

"The next step in this process was for man to elevate some of the more powerful spirits to gods. These were spirits that could be worshipped, that man believed he could influence by sacrifice, ritual or prayer. For example the Babylonians worshipped the heavenly bodies and used their names for the days of the week. This reverence has survived in the words Sunday, Monday and Saturday for sun, moon and Saturn. The earth, too, was believed to be a god. In Fiji, for example, earthquakes were thought to be caused by the earth-god turning over in his sleep. Trees were worshipped almost universally. In the Molucca islands no loud noises were allowed near trees for fear that they might drop their fruit prematurely."

The Archaeologist made a gesture interrupting the Historian. "Let's not forget the greatest fear and mystery

10

of them all: death. When primitive man dreamed about a person who had recently died, he created the idea of the soul. You see, when he saw his father, for example, in a dream, he believed that the spirit of his father was not dead but that it continued to live long after the body had died."

I stood still. "Are you saying, gentlemen, that this was universal among ancient people?"

The Historian motioned me to walk on. "There were some exceptions, but very few. In fact these beliefs can still be traced in primitive tribes today. You mustn't forget that primitive man depended on the environment much more than we do today. If there was a drought or a bad crop he felt very much dependent on the gods."

"You are not implying that the religion of the people in the Old Testament started in this way too, are you?"

The Historian took his pipe out of his jacket and lit it. Then looking at me through the smoke he said: "We are not only implying this, Mr. Penter, we know it for certain. The Old Testament starts at a time when the people in it were a Bedouin tribe in the desert. They worshipped a multitude of gods very much like those of other primitive peoples of Africa, Europe or even North America."

We entered the inn and sat down at a table.

"Then how did Judaism come into existence?" I asked.

"Look," the Historian said, "I realize this is not easy to take for most people. I am afraid the picture archaeologists and historians have been able to piece together from their discoveries is a bit different from what you learned in Sunday school."

I nodded.

"All right then. What you should realize is that printing was not invented until about 1450 AD. Before that time books were written by hand on papyrus or leather rolls. But these rolls didn't last very long. So they were copied and recopied. This produced errors, especially in Hebrew, which had no vowels, only consonants. But much more important in this copying process is the fact that it made it inviting for later generations to edit the books according to their own opinions and, of course, only books that were of interest to later generations were copied. The others disappeared. For this reason we cannot trust the books of the Old Testament entirely. Fortunately we have some stonewritings and clay tablets from other civilizations of that area which are originals and provide a more reliable albeit indirect source.

"Now then, let's go back to the time of Moses, about 1300 BC. We don't know why the Jewish people went to Egypt, whether it was a voluntary emigration or whether they were brought there as slaves. All we know is that, before Egypt they had roamed the area east of Egypt as one of many Semitic tribes. In their wanderings they had taken over many of the religious beliefs of neighboring peoples. They worshipped rocks, cattle, sheep, snakes and even the spirit of caves and hills. Yahweh, who later became the sole God of Judaism and Christianity—wrongly translated as Jehovah—was initially just one of many gods. He was the god of lightning and war and received human sacrifice, especially first-born male children."

I looked at the Historian, startled. He went on matter-of-factly. "In Egypt there appears Moses. The facts concerning Moses are few. No mention of him is made by the later authors Amos and Isaiah, and it is very doubtful that he was in fact the author of the books ascribed to him. Manetho, an Egyptian historian of the third century BC states that the exodus of the Israelites was due to the desire of the Egyptians to protect themselves from a plague which had broken out among the Jewish people in Egypt, and that Moses was an Egyptian priest who went along as a missionary. The name Moses is in fact of Egyptian origin.

12

"At about the time of Moses an Egyptian pharaoh, Amonhotep IV, revolutionized the religion of Egypt by forbidding worship of the chief god Amon and the thousands of other gods, and putting in their place Aton, a single god. He changed his own name to Ikhnaton and ordered that all references to Amon be chiseled from the monuments. But Ikhnaton died after a reign of only 18 years and the priests of Amon convinced his successor, Tutenkhamen, better known as King Tut, to revert back to polytheism. Whether or not Moses was influenced by the religion of Aton is uncertain, but it is curious that one of the Psalms, Psalm 104, is identical to a poem found on an Egyptian monument dedicated to Aton.

"So the Jews leave Egypt for whatever reason under Moses' leadership and spend 40 years like Bedouins in the desert. Moses tries desperately to change his people from polytheism to a belief in Yahweh, but succeeds only partially. He brings down from the mountain ten commandments for his people which he says were given to him by Yahweh."

"You may be interested to know," interjected the Archaeologist, "that such laws, said to have originated directly from a god, were common to a number of religions at that time."

"Quite true," said the Historian. "In Persia the book of law was, according to legend, delivered to Zoroaster on a mountain in thunder and lightning. The Cretan myth has King Minos receive the law from his god on Mount Dicta; and in Greece Dionysius is called the law-giver and is pictured as holding two tablets of stone in which the laws have been chiseled. But let me go on.

"When Moses dies, Joshua takes over and leads the Jewish people into Canaan. Joshua, unlike Moses, is a warrior. He attacks and decimates the inhabitants of Canaan to make room for himself and his people. After Joshua the conquering continues for a period of some 200 years and the conquered land is divided into 12 areas for the 12 tribes of Israel.

"Then, around 1020 BC Saul makes himself the first king of Israel. He is succeeded by David, who establishes Jerusalem as the capital. After David's death in 962 BC his son, Solomon ascends to the throne. He builds the first temple and a large palace for himself, where he is said to have lived with 60 wives and 80 concubines. After his death in 935 BC the kingdom splits into two rivaling halves: Ephraim, also called Israel, with Samaria as capital, and Judah, of which Jerusalem was the capital.

"From this point on and for a period of 400 years the history of the Jewish people is marred by internal strife, religious decay and wars. Of the 19 kings, 8 were assassinated. Jerusalem was captured first by Egypt and then by the Assyrians. This was the time of the prophets, a term in those days that did not mean seer. These were social critics who tried to bring the people of Israel back to belief in Yahweh, and to inspire trust in the people for the future of Israel as a nation.

"Nebuchadnezzar, king of Babylon, overran Judah several times and finally destroyed Jerusalem in 582 BC and deported the entire population to Babylon. It was during this time that the prophet Jeremiah wrote his book to fight the influence of the Babylonian religion. Babylonia at that time was a rich country with fertile soil; life for the Jews there was quite pleasant and many of them grew rich. It is, therefore, no surprise if, by the second generation of the exile, Babylonian customs started to predominate. This is what Jeremiah and an unknown writer who completed the book of Isaiah were fighting against.

"In 538 Cyrus of Persia entered Babylonia and freed the Jews. But they were not too anxious to return to Jerusalem. And when, after two years the first caravans arrived back in Judah, they found the land occupied by foreigners. Slowly they rebuilt Jerusalem and the temple.

14

But the glory of former times was gone. It was a lawless state, without a king or military power and with intermarriage with foreigners. Moreover low morale threatened the survival of Israel as an entity.

"It was at this low point of fortune that the Old Testament came into existence. Ezra, a prophet who had returned from Babylonia in one of the later caravans, called the people together and read them the 'Law of Moses,' a series of scrolls that became the law of Israel and has been able to hold its people together for more than 2400 years.

"What was this 'Law of Moses'? Very likely it was what we now call the Torah or the Pentateuch, the five books of Moses. Where did Ezra get them? We don't know. About 200 years earlier, during the reign of king Josiah, the high-priest Hilkiah is said to have 'found' a scroll in the temple which was called the 'Book of the Covenant.' But the Book of the Covenant took only half a day to read, whereas it took 'seven days from morn to midday' to read the Law of Moses. We don't have to assume that Ezra simply made up the additional material. More likely a large number of scrolls describing the history of Israel, its legends, customs, rules was already in circulation and Ezra combined what was needed at the moment.

"The Law of Moses was not just a religious document. It was the civil and criminal law, it regulated personal hygiene, diet, medicine, public sanitation, sex and marriage. Rather than a description of the Jewish life, it was a priestly utopia, an admirable document and one of the jewels of literature."

The Historian sat back and looked at me intently.

"But from an historian's point of view," he continued slowly, "there is no difference between it and, for example, Greek literature. It is a collection of ancient legends, handed down verbally through generations, added to and changed many times, influenced by contacts with other

15

cultures, and finally written down and copied and re-copied. It's a tale, belonging to legend and myth."

"Wrong, wrong, wrong," a voice said behind us. A trim young man stood there.

"And who are you?" I asked.

"Josh McDowell."

"You don't agree with the Historian's point of view?" I asked.

"Not in the least. He is completely biased and has left out some very important ideas that change the whole picture. For example, the Bible is by far the most reliable document we have about those times, far more reliable than he wants you to believe. In transcribing the Old Testament very elaborate rules were followed by the Talmudists. Every roll had to contain a certain number of columns, the breadth of each column had to consist of thirty letters, an authentic copy had to be the exemplar, from which the transcriber could not deviate in the least. No word or letter was to be written from memory, between every consonant the space of a hair was to intervene, and the writer was to sit in full Jewish dress while copying . . . "

"The Talmudists didn't start copying the Torah until 100 AD," interrupted the Historian.

"That's true," McDowell answered, "but it shows the great respect for accuracy the Jewish people had."

"That proves nothing. At that point the Old Testament had become a sacred book. The crucial time is the early period, a thousand years before the Talmudists, where we know nothing about transcription or how much of it was written down or whether it was merely oral folklore."

McDowell continued. "You historians and archaeologists seem to have singled out the Old Testament for criticism. No one seems to question the authenticity of Caesar or Plato, even though the earliest extant copies of

16

their works were written some 900 years after their deaths. The earliest copy of Aristotle dates from 1100 AD, some 1450 years after his death. But for the Old Testament we have copies as old as 100 BC.''

McDowell turned to the Archaeologist. "Isn't it true that archaeology has confirmed many, many of the facts in the Old Testament?''

"That's true,'' the Archaeologist answered, "I have to admit that. As far as times, places and people are concerned, the Old Testament is a remarkably accurate document.''

"There, you see! Even one of your most distinguished colleagues, Sir Frederic Kenyon, who was director of the British Museum, said that archaeology has re-established the authority of the Old Testament.''

"Well, now, wait just a minute,'' the Archaeologist said, "You seem to mention only what is favorable to your case. Frederic Kenyon also says that the Old Testament is a 'collection of books of uncertain origin which were not put together in the present form until sometime between the ninth and the second century BC'. He also stated the opinion that the text of the Old Testament was certain to have suffered corruption and that Moses was not the author of the Pentateuch, the five books of Moses.''

"Well, you see, there I disagree with Kenyon,'' McDowell said heatedly. "I am convinced that Moses was the author of the Pentateuch. Oh, I don't mean that he wrote it himself, in his own hand. He probably dictated it to scribes. That's why it is written in the third person. There is abundant evidence for this. Joshua speaks of the 'Law of Moses', which he had written. There are similar references in Kings, Chronicles, Ezra, Daniel and Malachi. The apostles in the New Testament certainly believed that Moses was the author.''

The Archaeologist smiled mischievously, got up and

came back with a book in his hand. "Just so there is no mistake, you claim that Moses was the author of the first five books of the Bible, that he wrote them—or dictated them—during his lifetime. Right?"

"Right."

"Let us take Exodus, Mr. McDowell. I am sure you know in great detail the plagues that Yahweh struck on Egypt."

"Of course."

"Could you explain this, then?" the Archaeologist had opened the book and held it in front of McDowell, pointing to a paragraph.

"What is there to explain?"

"Well, why don't you read it so that everyone knows what paragraph we are talking about."

McDowell read: "If you refuse to let them go and still keep your hold on them, the Lord will strike your grazing herds, your horses and asses, your camels, cattle and sheep with a terrible pestilence. But the Lord will make a distinction between Israel's herds and those of the Egyptians. Of all that belongs to Israel not a single one shall die. The Lord fixed a time and said: tomorrow I will do this throughout the land. The next day the Lord struck. And all the herds of Egypt died, but from the herds of Israel not a single beast died."

"That's far enough," the Archaeologist said, "now three chapters and five plagues later, Exodus 12:29."

McDowell searched for the passage. "And by midnight the Lord struck down every first-born in Egypt, from the first-born of Pharaoh on his throne to the first-born of the captive in the dungeon and the first-born of cattle . . . "

"Don't you see it, Mr. McDowell?" the Archaeologist asked.

"See what?" McDowell asked.

"God had already killed all the cattle, how could he kill the first-born of the cattle again?"

McDowell wrinkled his forehead.

"But go on, read chapter 14, verses 8 and 9," the Archaeologist said.

"Then Pharaoh, king of Egypt, made obstinate by the Lord, pursued the Israelites as they marched defiantly away. The Egyptians, all Pharaoh's chariots and horses, cavalry and infantry, pursued them . . ."

"There it is again," the Archaeologist jumped in, "horses. God had already killed all the horses in the second plague."

The Archaeologist sat back. "I don't mean to ridicule the Bible, Mr. McDowell, but there are so many inconsistencies. It seems to me this is a story written by an uncritical, primitive people."

"May I add something to this, gentlemen?"

Behind the Archaeologist stood a slight man with a pronounced nose, thin lips and hair drawn straight back, his clothes in the style of the 18th century.

I had seen this face before. He had something to do with the American Revolution. A writer. Then I suddenly remembered. "Thomas Paine," I burst out.

Paine bowed toward me and then faced McDowell. "Have you ever read my book *The Age of Reason*?"

"Certainly not, sir," McDowell answered, "you were an atheist!"

"I am afraid you are misinformed, sir, I was not an atheist. I believed in God, I was a deist. It is a pity that you did not read *The Age of Reason*. You could have saved yourself a considerable amount of work."

Paine took the book lying on the table and opened it. "I assume you are familiar with Genesis, Mr. McDowell."

"I most certainly am."

"Good. Then would you be so kind as to read Genesis 14:14?"

McDowell took the book, looked around the table and started reading: "When Abraham heard that his kinsmen had been taken prisoner, he mustered his retainers, men born in his household, 318 of them, and pursued as far as Dan."

"Thank you," said Paine, "now I would like you to read this passage from Judges, chapter 18, verses 27 to 29."

McDowell read: "Thus they carried off the priest and the things Micah had made for himself, and attacked Laish, whose people were quiet and carefree. They put them to the sword and set fire to the city. There was no one to save them, for the city was a long way from Sidon and they had no contact with the Aramaeans, although the city was in the vale near Beth-rehob. They rebuilt the city and settled in it, naming it Dan after the name of their forefather Dan, a son of Israel; but its original name was Laish."

"Do you know when this took place?" Paine asked.

"About 1100 BC, I think," McDowell answered.

"In other words more than 200 years after Moses! Then how could Moses have known that the name of the city was Dan?"

McDowell looked at the book again to check the passage. Paine pointed to the paragraph and said: "Right here Moses calls the city Dan. Yet in the same Old Testament it says that the city's name was Laish at the time of Moses and its name wasn't changed to Dan until 200 years after Moses was dead."

"Let's take another paragraph," Paine said without waiting for an answer. "Genesis, chapter 36, verse 31."

Paine flipped the pages for McDowell who reluctantly took it and started to read: "These are the kings who ruled over Edom before there were any kings in Israel: Bela, son of Beor . . ."

"No need to go any further," said Paine.

20

"I don't understand," said McDowell, puzzled.

"Who was the first king of Israel, Mr. McDowell?" Paine asked.

"Why, Saul, of course," McDowell answered.

"When did he rule?"

"I think it was 1020 BC," said McDowell.

"Or about 300 years after Moses. Then how could Moses have known that there would be kings in Israel?"

"Well, of course God could have told him that," McDowell said.

"Or it could be, Mr. McDowell," Paine continued, "that this account was not written until after the time of Saul."

Paine abruptly took the book from McDowell and flipped the pages. "Exodus, chapter 16, verse 34, also written by Moses according to you: 'The Israelites ate the manna for forty years until they came to a land where they could settle; they ate until they came to the border of Canaan'. Mr. McDowell, didn't Moses die before the Israelites reached Canaan?"

"Yes, he did," said McDowell.

"Then how could Moses write that they ate manna until they came to the border of Canaan?"

"Deuteronomy, also a book of Moses, chapter 34, verses 5 and 6: 'There in the land of Moab Moses, the servant of the Lord, died, as the Lord had said. He was buried in a valley in Moab opposite Beth-peor, but to this day no one knows his burial place'. Mr. McDowell, Moses reporting his own death and burial? And what does that mean: to this day? Only somebody writing much later would write 'to this day'!"

McDowell looked at the historian, the Archaeologist and then at me. "My motivation, gentlemen, is to glorify and magnify Christ, not to win an argument!" He got up and walked away.

"Well, that's too bad," Paine said, "I had a few more

questions for Mr. McDowell. About the Creation, Joshua, Samuel, David, Solomon, Miracles and the New Testament."

"Mr. Paine," I asked, "did you believe in God?"

"Yes, I believed in God," Paine answered, "in one God, but no more. And I hoped for happiness after life."

"I wish you could tell us if you found that happiness," the Historian said.

Paine didn't answer.

"But you rejected all the Christian scriptures?" I asked.

"Yes, especially the Old Testament. I was disturbed by the idea of revelation. Revelation means something communicated directly from God to man. I don't dispute that the Almighty has the power to make such a communication. But even if it took place, which I doubt, it was revelation only to the first person. When he tells it to a second, a second to a third, a third to a fourth and so on, it ceases to be revelation, it becomes hearsay.

"We are not obliged to believe that Moses received the tables of commandment from the hands of God, because there are many similar claims in other religions. For example it is claimed that the Koran was written in heaven and brought to Mahomet by an angel.

"But the worst thing about the Old Testament is that it is incredible and shocking. It is full of obscene stories, debaucheries, cruel and tortuous executions and vindictiveness. Let's take Joshua, for example, the successor of Moses. In Jericho he ordered that everyone be put to the sword, men and women, young and old, also cattle, sheep and asses. In Ai the Israelites massacred the entire population, twelve thousand of them and hanged the king. In Makkedah they beheaded five kings who had been hiding in a cave and hung their bodies on trees. Then they captured the city and destroyed every living thing in it. They did the same in Libuah; it says that they left no survivors there. And they repeated this at Lachish, Gezer, Eglon, Hebron and Debir.''

Thomas Paine grabbed the book and opened it. ''And then, and I quote: 'Joshua massacred the population of the whole region—the hill country, the Negeb, the Shepelah, the watersheds—and all their kings. He left no survivors, destroying everything that drew breath, as the Lord, the God of Israel had commanded. Joshua carried the slaughter from Kadesh-barnea to Gaza, over the whole land of Goshen and as far as Gibeon'.''

Paine put the book down and looked at me. ''I ask you, how could a loving, caring God order the killing of men, women, children and animals who had done nothing wrong except to live there?''

Thomas Paine abruptly bowed and disappeared.

Nobody spoke for a minute.

''Alright,'' I said, sitting up straight. ''So maybe the Old Testament contains some folklore and was influenced by human beings in later times. That doesn't mean it couldn't have originated from God, does it?''

''But, Mr. Penter,'' the Archaeologist replied, ''there are so many ancient documents that claim divine origin.''

''Yes, but the Old Testament is by far the oldest, is it not?''

''No, as a matter of fact it isn't,'' the Historian answered. ''If you take Homer's *Iliad,* for example, it was written about the same time, tells about people and gods in the same time period and fulfilled the same purpose for the Greek people as the Pentateuch for the Jewish people: it was the central religious and historical document. But there is something else.''

''What is that?''

''Almost all of the stories in the Pentateuch can be traced to earlier civilizations. The Babylonians, for example, had strikingly similar accounts of creation already in the 21st century BC, long before Moses. They also had ten

23

patriarchs or kings, also with very long lifetimes. The tenth king also built an ark and the story of the flood is almost identical. I am afraid the evidence points overwhelmingly to the Hebrew story as a copy, changed and adapted to their particular religion. I would say that this makes revelation extremely doubtful. We have known this for a hundred years, Mr. Penter."

"If you are correct," I said slowly, "then the whole thing doesn't make sense. I mean, how could half the world, for 2000 or 3000 years, revere as God-inspired and sacred a document that you say is man-made? How could such a thing ever happen? What would have motivated these people to produce a fraud? It's inconceivable to me."

The Historian took out his notepad and wrote something down. He tore off the sheet and gave it to me. "I want to warn you that this man's theory is, so far, unproven. It's a hypothesis. But maybe it will open your mind and give you a clue. Go and see him."

The paper read: Julian Jaynes, Princeton University.

* * *

A tall man of 50 with a deep voice sat across from me. "I understand you are a lecturer in psychology, specializing in consciousness," I asked him.

"That's correct," Jaynes said.

"And in your research on consciousness you found something concerning the origin of religion? Could you explain that to me?"

"First we have to examine the human brain. For reasons we don't clearly understand the brain is divided into two symmetrical halves. The left half controls the right side of the body, arm, leg, touch sensation, eye, whereas the right side of the brain controls the left side of the body. This crossconnection is true for all functions except speech. For almost all right-handed individuals speech is controlled only by the left side of the brain, chiefly in three areas of the left hemisphere, the most important of which is called Wernicke's area, located roughly above the left ear. For most left-handed people this is reversed; speech is controlled by the corresponding areas in the right hemisphere. To avoid confusion, I shall assume that all people are right-handed; what I am about to say is simply reversed for left-handed people.

"Now the curious thing is that the portion of the brain corresponding to Wernicke's area in the right hemisphere doesn't seem to be doing anything; the same area in the left hemisphere appears to be doing all the work. The area in the right hemisphere can be removed without causing a loss of speech. But if Wernicke's area in the left hemisphere is injured or removed, the person can no longer talk; if a person is young enough, speech will be relearned using Wernicke's area in the right hemisphere.

"There is a clue, however, as to what Wernicke's area in the right hemisphere does and this comes from research done with schizophrenic people. Almost all schizophrenics have hallucinations; they hear voices and occasionally, though less frequently, see images."

"You mean like in dreams?" I asked.

"No," Jaynes answered, "not like in dreams. These are voices that a schizophrenic hears during waking hours and perceives to be real. When a schizophrenic has a hallucination, there is someone who is talking to him. He can clearly hear it, as if the person were standing in the room. To a schizophrenic this voice is part of reality."

"Such voices are heard sometimes even by perfectly normal people. A study done in England in the last century revealed that about 8% of all men and 12% of all women had such an experience at least once during their life. It seems to happen with greatest frequency in the age group 20 to 29, which is also true for schizophrenics.

"The trigger for such a hallucination is always stress. Sometimes the voice can be prophetic. For example, the voice tells the patient that someone is about to enter the room. What seems to happen in such cases is that the patient subconsciously hears a noise in the hallway and before he realizes what this noise means, the voice he hears tells him.

"The interesting thing is that these hallucinations can be produced artificially even in normal people by stimulating Wernicke's area in the right hemisphere with a weak electric current. Only stimulation of that particular area causes this. Penfield reported this in 1963. He did a study on 70 people who were about to undergo brain surgery. A 15-year-old girl, for example, when stimulated in the area cried out: 'Everybody is shouting at me again, make them stop'. A 36-year-old woman heard 'voices down along the river', a river she thought she visited as a child. A 24-year-old woman said during the stimulation: 'That man's voice again! The only thing I know is that my father frightens me a lot'. In most cases, though, the voices were hazy and hard to recognize.

"It appears that previous experience is stored in that area and 're-played' during periods of stress, especially in schizophrenic people, without any conscious will or command. There is a connection between the two halves of the brain in about that area, 1/8 of an inch in diameter, called the anterior commissure. If this connection is cut in schizophrenic people, the hallucination is stopped and never occurs again. It must be then that, for these people in times of stress, the previous experience is replayed through the anterior commissure into the speech area in the left hemisphere.

"Now these voices are not just straight experiences from the past. In general, for other brain functions, the right hemisphere does the sorting out of experience. It fits the bits and pieces of experience together into a complete whole that tells people what to do. For example, we use primarily the right half of the brain to solve puzzles and mazes. A person with an injury to the right side of the brain can no longer do that, though in all other respect he or she will appear normal.

"For this reason the voices that schizophrenic people hallucinate aren't just straight experiences, they tell them what to do; they admonish them, they yell at them, they chide, they dictate. They represent the authority of experience, subconsciously combined and coordinated.

"All this has a lot to do with speech, language. Language started quite recently, probably, in a crude form around 40,000 BC. Sentence structures with nouns appeared probably between 25,000 BC and 15,000 BC.

"The most important event in the development of language, in my opinion, was the creation of names. This probably happened quite late, perhaps between 10,000 and 8,000 BC in Mesopotamia, Egypt and Greece and at different times in other parts of the world. Once a tribe member had a proper name, he could be remembered, could be recreated in his absence. And I believe that it was when people started to use names that Wernicke's area in the right hemisphere began to play its strange role. There is strong evidence that, at that time, this area of the brain was far more influential than it is today, that hallucinations caused by it were far more frequent than they are today, and that it was in fact such hallucinations which were interpreted by primitive people as the voices of the gods. Not just dreams, but actual hallucinations during waking hours.

"In ancient times, when a person who heard the voice of someone who was, in fact, dead, he believed that this person was not dead, but merely transfigured. That is why we find in so many graves and tombs of that time food, clothing, even furniture, chariots, animals and slaves.

"And since many of these voices he did not recognize

and since they were commanding, admonishing, told him what to do, these voices became the gods. We have ample proof of that in the earliest literature, the Greek *Iliad,* for example. In this story there are no conscious plans, no motives, there is no reason; everything is caused by the speeches of the gods. Achilles says: 'What could I do? The gods always have their ways'. We find this phenomenon in all the first literature of early civilizations, including the Old Testament. Yahweh speaks to Moses, tells him what to do.

"The second part of the evidence is found in statues and pictures of gods from that time. These images are seen speaking to the people, their mouths open. And we also find houses and temples which were built where a god had spoken or was speaking to the people.

"One of the most recent records of this phenomenon we have is from the subjugation of the Incas by the Spaniards in 1532. The Spaniards reported that the devil spoke to the Incas out of the mouths of statues and in the temple in a dark room. The Incas were at this time at a stage in their development which the Spaniards and other more advanced civilizations had experienced several thousand years earlier. It is because the Incas were still guided by the voices of their gods that a band of only 150 Spaniards was able to conquer their whole empire.

"In the religious images of Egypt, Assyria and others we can also see how this phenomenon slowly disappeared, how the voices of the gods became silent."

"What caused this change?" I asked.

"Two things happened," Jaynes answered, "writing and trade. Before writing was invented the hallucinated voice was the sole authority. But when the records of previous voices in the scriptures contradicted the present voice, people started to doubt its authority.

"Trade brought contact with other civilizations, who had different commands from their gods, causing more

28

conflict. This disintegration took place during the time of the Old Testament. It was probably one of the most confusing times in human history. Before, life was simple, people followed the direction of their gods who spoke during times of stress whenever decisions needed to be made. Then, as writing spread and more and more contact was made with other cultures, the voices became less and less frequent; the people felt lost, abandoned by their gods. In a way that is what religion is: a longing to be guided by a god as man once was for a period of a few thousand years between the creation of language and the advent of writing. This longing is still in us today."

"Mr. Jaynes, did the brain then change with the arrival of writing? I mean, is our brain different from that of the people then?" I asked.

"Well," said Jaynes, "yes and no. The outermost and largest portion of the human brain, the neocortex, is formed, or programmed so to speak, in early childhood. We know that this process is very flexible or, rather, adaptable. For example, if an area of the brain of a very small child is injured, the function normally assigned to this area can be performed by a different area of the brain. In a similar way the arrival of writing displaced some other function in the brain, it changed the relative allocations of brain areas, though there was no change in appearance or size."

"Let me try to understand this," I said. "Your theory says that, long after man had evolved from the ape and acquired his large brain, after he had invented language, the structure of his brain caused him to hear voices, like schizophrenic people still do today."

"That's right."

"And he could not help but believe that these voices were real."

"Just as schizophrenic people today believe the voices they hear are real."

"And because it was a real experience and these voices often criticized and admonished and occasionally even appeared to be prophetic, primitive man was guided by them, built monuments to them, made them into gods and later wrote about them."

"That's right."

An Intermission

You have probably noticed that there are two kinds of characters in this story. The Archaeologist and the Historian and similar characters in the following chapters reflect a composite of the works listed in the bibliography at the end of the book.

Characters with individual names are real people—writers who present their own point of view, whenever possible exactly as they wrote it.

Some of these writers are contemporaries of ours, others have been dead for centuries. I use an author's prerogative and make no distinction in time, I let them float in and out of the present, sometimes on the flimsiest of pretexts. You may safely assume that none of these encounters ever took place, except in my mind.

Another point: This book is by no means a balanced treatise. It assumes that you have been exposed to the Jewish-Christian teachings and hence need no refresher course on commonplace knowledge. I only want to bring up what is not generally known—what we have not been told, yet should have been.

Each chapter has a different setting to examine the topics of the subject from different angles. The next chapter is about philosophy, very likely the most difficult chapter of the book. If you are not philosophically inclined and find yourself stuck, skip over it. Perhaps you can come back to it later; but even if you don't, you have missed a part which is only important for completeness, not for the understanding of the following chapters.

2
The Proof

My eyes were wandering across the row of books in the great library. I had been reading for hours and, so far, I had not found what I was looking for. But I was determined to continue. With all the great philosophers and theologians that the past 20 centuries had produced, there must be at least one simple, convincing proof of God's existence.

"It's not that easy." The voice came from behind my back and I turned around sharply. A man stood there I had not noticed before.

"I beg your pardon?"

"It's not easy to prove the existence of God in a purely rational way."

"How did you know that's what I was after? Who are you?"

"I am your Mentor."

"My Mentor? I didn't know I had a Mentor. Who are you really?"

"It doesn't matter who I am. You need a Mentor. In this part of your search you need help."

I was taken back by his appearance but was resolved to keep up normal appearance. "I take it my first impression is correct. These proofs are complicated and confusing."

"And it gets worse as you go on."

"All right then, Mentor, what should I do?"

"St. Anselm of Canterbury." The Mentor walked toward the bookstack and pulled out an old, leatherbound volume. "He was the originator of one of the three great arguments for the existence of God. Born in 1033 in Aosta in northern Italy, he entered the Benedictine monastery at Bec, France in 1060, became its Prior in 1063 and its Abbott in 1078. In 1093 he was made Archbishop of Canterbury."

"Canterbury, England? How does an Italian become a monk in France and an Archbishop in England?"

"I can answer that." Suddenly a tall figure dressed in a white habit had appeared behind the Mentor. "I went to the abbey of Ste. Marie du Bec because of Lafranc, who was one of the most famous theologians at that time. He was then Prior and I wanted to study under him. The abbey was supported financially by many noblemen, among them William the Conqueror, who granted us landholdings in England. We founded many other monasteries, both in France and in England. And so Lafranc was named Archbishop of Canterbury and I succeeded him."

I looked at the Mentor, suspecting a hoax.

The Mentor was not perturbed. "This young man is looking for proof of God's existence. I thought you might tell him what you wrote in your *Proslogion*."

"What is a *Proslogion*?" I asked.

"While at Bec," Anselm replied in a measured voice, "I wrote two pamphlets or short books. The first one I called the *Monologion,* the second the *Proslogion,* which means addition or sequence. In this second volume I described a proof for the existence of God by reason alone."

"I'm all ears."

St. Anselm looked at me intently. "First we must be sure we know what we mean by the word God. My defini-

34

tion, in your language, is this: We cannot conceive of anything greater than God.''

He paused and looked at me to make sure I had understood. I nodded thoughtfully. Seemed simple enough.

"Now let us take an unbeliever. In his heart this unbeliever says: there is no God! But if I talk to this unbeliever about the greatest thing that we can possibly conceive of, he understands what he hears, does he not? It is in his understanding, in his imagination, even if he does not know it. You see, it is one thing for a concept to be in his imagination and quite another for him to understand what that concept is.''

"That seems to be a bit tricky," I said. "Do you mean that I can talk to this unbeliever. He hears what I am saying but he does not understand what I am saying?''

"Not quite," St. Anselm said patiently. "Take a painter, for example. When a painter imagines what he is going to paint he has in his understanding what he has not yet painted. After he has painted it he both has it in his understanding and he understands that what he has now painted actually exists.''

"Okay, so far," I nodded.

"Now even an unbeliever must admit that the greatest thing that can be conceived exists at least in his imagination.''

St. Anselm paused to let it sink in.

"Now answer me this, Mr. Penter: which is greater, something that you only imagine or something that really exists?''

"I would say something that really exists.''

"Correct. And now comes the crucial point: if this unbeliever can imagine the greatest thing that can be conceived, this thing cannot be in his imagination alone, it must also exist in reality. If this wasn't true, then the thing which he has imagined would no longer be the greatest. This greatest thing is what we speak of as God.''

A monk appeared behind St. Anselm, shaking his head. "Not convincing.''

St. Anselm turned around and sighed: "Not you again, Gaunilo.''

"Yes, me again, Prior. Consider this, Mr. Penter: Someone tells me that somewhere in the ocean there is an island which is more abundantly filled with riches and delight than any other island and that, although it has no owner or inhabitant, it excells all the lands that men inhabit taken together in the unceasing abundance of its fertility.

"When this person tells me that there is such an island I easily understand what is being said. Suppose, however, that this person goes on to say: you cannot doubt that this island, which is more excellent than any other land, actually exists in reality. If this wasn't true then this island, which you understand to be the most excellent of all, would then not be the most excellent!''

Gaunilo's face said: try to top this!

"If anyone discovers for me,'' St. Anselm replied in a lofty voice, "something existing either in fact or in thought of which greater cannot be conceived and is able to apply the logic of my argument to it, I shall find that lost island and give it to him!''

"What St. Anselm means, Mr. Penter,'' the Mentor quickly said, "is that it is ridiculous to apply the reasoning of his argument to the island. It can only be applied to the greatest thing imaginable.''

I thought for a second. "I'm not sure I agree with this, though. I think maybe we are hung up on language.''

The Mentor took me by the arm. "That is the main problem in any of these arguments. But let me introduce you to someone who was very influential, yet didn't believe in this argument.''

36

The Mentor replaced the book in the stack and pulled out another one. I looked back; both St. Anselm and Gaunilo had disappeared.

"You will be most impressed by this thinker," the Mentor continued. "He was born some 200 years after St. Anselm. He was one of the greatest Christian philosophers; his work fills 54 volumes. Three hundred years after his death he was named a Doctor of the Church and in 1879 Pope Leo XIII gave his philosophy official papal approval."

A tall, serene and ascetic looking man in a black robe came walking toward me.

"May I introduce: St. Thomas Aquinas."

St. Thomas bowed.

I did the same, awkwardly.

"St. Thomas was born in Aquino, Italy, in 1224. He studied at the University of Naples where he joined the Dominican order. At age 21 he was sent to Paris where he studied under the famous Albertus Magnus. It was there that he started reading Aristotle and incorporated much of Aristotle's philosophy into his own. Father Thomas, would you care to help Mr. Penter with St. Anselm's argument?"

"Well," St. Thomas began, "first let me restate St. Anselm's proof in my own way. Those things are said to be self-evident which are known as soon as the terms are known. For example, when the nature of a whole and of a part are known, it is at once recognized that the whole is greater than the part. But as soon as the significance of the name God is understood, St. Anselm claims, it is at once seen that God exists. For by this name is signified the greatest thing which can be conceived. And that which exists mentally and actually is greater than that which exists mentally only. Therefore, as soon as the name God is understood, it must exist mentally, and it follows then, that it also must exist actually. Hence, the proposition that God exists is self-evident. Is my restatement correct?"

"Yes, and very concise," the Mentor replied.

"Now my answer to this statement is as follows: A thing can be self-evident in either of two ways. On the one hand it can be self-evident in itself and to us; on the other it can be self-evident in itself but not to us."

"This is very difficult to understand," I interjected.

"We want to examine if the statement 'God exists' is self-evident. This statement consists of a predicate and subject. God is the subject, exists is the predicate. Now a statement like that is self-evident if the predicate is included in the essence of the subject.

"Let me use an example, the statement: man is an animal. That is self-evident because animal is contained in the essence of man. What I am saying is that, if the essence of the subject is known to us, such a statement is self-evident in itself and to us.

"But if there are some to whom the essence of the subject is not known, then a statement may be self-evident in itself but not to those who do not know the meaning of the subject; and because we do not know the essence of God, St. Anselm's argument is not self-evident to us."

"In other words," the Mentor said, "you are rejecting St. Anselm's argument entirely."

"I am," said St. Thomas.

"I understand you formulated some different proofs for the existence of God," I said.

"Yes, would you like to hear them?"

"Perhaps we should do this later," the Mentor broke in, "you see St. Anselm's argument was revived in a somewhat different form after St. Thomas. I suggest we follow that thread and listen to St. Thomas later."

"That's fine with me," I said.

"Would you like to take a seat, Father Thomas?" the

Mentor asked and motioned St. Thomas to a nearby lounge chair. He then searched for another book.

"The fellow you are going to meet next is a very illustrious one: Gottfried Willhelm Leibniz."

"Ah, yes," I responded enthusiastically, "I have certainly heard of Leibniz. He is one of my heroes."

"Thank you," said the voice next to me. There stood Gottfried Willhelm Leibniz, a bit paunchy, with a large nose and a huge black wig. His appearance was pompous. But, I figured, that was the way people of his stature dressed in his days.

A group of curious onlookers gathered, attracted by the spectacle of Leibniz at one end and St. Thomas sitting quietly in his chair at the other.

"You say you know Mr. Leibniz?," the Mentor asked.

"Yes, I do," I answered, ready to show off, "he was born about 1650 I believe. . . ."

"1646," Leibniz corrected.

"1646. He was one of the most brilliant men ever. In fact it is said of him that he was the last man who had the entire knowledge of mankind in his head."

Leibniz bowed and smiled in a self-assured way.

"He made contributions in law, politics, physics, mechanics, mining and geology. In fact you were the first one to propose that the earth has a molten core, were you not?"

"Indeed I was."

"And chemistry," I continued, "history, philosophy and, above all, mathematics. You invented the binary system and differential and integral calculus, did you not?"

One of the onlookers quickly said: "I thought Newton invented that."

"Who said that?" Leibniz asked sharply.

"Didn't Isaac Newton invent the differential and integral calculus?" a student asked.

"Not so," Leibniz said, raising his voice, "I did! It is a confounded lie that I stole it from him."

"Alright, alright," the Mentor intervened, "no need to get excited. We are quite willing to accept that it was invented independently by you and Isaac Newton."

"You should teach your youth to be more respectful," Leibniz added, still fuming. He pulled an embroidered handkerchief out of his sleeve and patted his forehead.

"What most people don't know," the Mentor said, "is that Mr. Leibniz also made valuable contributions in theology. Now then, Mr. Leibniz, Rene Descartes, who preceded you, restated the argument of St. Anselm and you developed his argument even further. Would you now give us your argument for the existence of God?"

"Certainly. First, let me make a definition: I call every simple quality which is positive and absolute, or expresses whatever it expresses without any limits, a perfection."

Leibniz made an elegant turn to see if his audience had followed. The onlooker who had previously spoken wrinkled his forehead and said: "In real life?"

The Mentor motioned him to be quiet and Leibniz continued.

"Now a quality of this sort, because it is simple, is irresolvable and indefinable. If it were not, it would not be a simple quality but an aggregate of many. Or, if it were resolvable or could be defined it would automatically have limits."

Some of the onlookers had blank stares on their faces.

"From these considerations it is not difficult to show that all perfections are compatible with each other or that they can exist in the same subject and therefore the most perfect being, God, can be known . . ."

"I don't follow this at all, sir," the same onlooker interrupted. "Your argument seems to make sense only in abstract mathematics. In reality we don't even know whether anything perfect can be assumed to exist. In all the history of science we have never run across anything that's perfect. Oh, we have always assumed at first that newly discovered things were perfect, such as the orbits of the planets or the shape of the earth, but we always seem to find variations, imperfection. Even atoms or subatomic particles are subject to statistical variations.''

"Subatomic particles?'' Leibniz asked, puzzled.

"I am sorry, sir, that came after your time,'' the onlooker laughed.

"But that doesn't mean God cannot be perfect.''

"No, it doesn't,'' I jumped in, "but it means that your argument is based on an assumption.''

"But in mathematical terms . . . '' Leibniz didn't get any further. Several of the onlookers started shouting and the debate continued among them. I looked at the Mentor and shook my head. Leibniz faded out.

"Gentlemen, please,'' the Mentor shouted and the debate stopped. "Would you mind? This is really a private discussion.''

The onlookers reluctantly moved away.

"What are subatomic particles?'' Saint Thomas asked quietly.

The Mentor smiled. "It's very complicated. If you don't mind I would like to conclude the present subject first.'' He pulled out a new book.

"I am sorry, I didn't mean to interrupt,'' said St. Thomas.

"Here we have a gentleman,'' the Mentor said, looking at me and holding up the book, "a university professor, who was born 78 years after Leibniz and who formulated an answer to the argument. He started as a lecturer in geography and astronomy, later switched to logic and metaphysics. May I introduce, from Koenigsberg, Germany: Immanuel Kant.''

The man who appeared was barely five feet tall and stooped.

"Why don't we all sit down," I suggested.

"Mr. Kant," the Mentor started, "from your *Critique of Pure Reason,* could you give us your answer to this argument?"

Kant cleared his throat.

"The confusion is in the language," he said, weighing every word. "If I say God is omnipotent, God is the subject, omnipotent is the predicate. The predicate describes or determines the subject.

"Now there are two kinds of predicates, the real or determining predicate, such as, in our case, omnipotent, and a logical predicate. Anything we please can be made into a logical predicate. The subject can be its own predicate, for example God is God. Logical, but it doesn't say anything.

"A determining predicate is added to a concept and enlarges it. A mere logical predicate does not. The word being is not a real predicate, it is only a logical one. In other words it is not something which adds to a concept.

"In the sentence 'God is omnipotent' the word 'is' is not a predicate, it doesn't add anything. It only serves to link the predicate to the subject. If we say 'God is' we haven't added anything to our concept of God.

"The concept of a supreme being is a very useful idea; but because it is a mere idea, it is incapable, by itself, of enlarging our knowledge in regards to what exists. It is not even able to enlighten us as to the possibility of any existence beyond what we know from experience."

"Language," I exclaimed, "language! The whole argument, going on for 750 years, is just a problem of language."

"That's right," Kant nodded.

"Does that settle it?" I asked the Mentor.

"It does," he replied and looked at Kant.

"Oh, do I have to go already?" Kant said sadly. "I would have liked to talk to St. Thomas for a while."

"Sorry, Mr. Kant," the Mentor said, "we need Father Thomas now."

"Thank you, Mr. Kant," I said and shook hands with him, and while I was doing so he disappeared.

* * *

"Father Thomas," the Mentor said, "in your *Summa Theologica* you list five ways by which the existence of God can be proven. They all express a common idea, now generally recognized as the second of the three great arguments. Since they are similar, would you explain one or two of them to Mr. Penter, perhaps the first and the third?"

"I'll be happy to," replied St. Thomas who straightened up in his chair. "The first is the argument from motion. It is certain and evident to our senses that in the world some things are in motion. Now, whatever is in motion has been moved by something else. The thing itself only has a potential to move. Motion itself is nothing else than the reduction of something of a potential to actuality. But to reduce something from a potential to actuality you need something in the state of actuality.

"Thus, that which is actually hot, namely fire, makes wood, which is potentially hot, actually hot, and thereby moves and changes it.

"Now it is not possible," he continued, "that the same thing should be in potentiality and actuality at the same time. For what is actually hot cannot be potentially hot at the same time; in fact once it is actually hot it can only be potentially cold.

"It is, therefore, impossible that a thing could be both mover and moved, that is that it should move itself. Hence, whatever is moved must be moved by something else. If that 'something else' is itself moved, then it too must have been moved by something else. But this cannot go on to infinity, because then there would be no first mover and consequently no other mover. Therefore it is necessary to arrive at a first mover, moved by no other. And this everybody understands to be God.''

St. Thomas leaned back in his chair and let the logic of his argument sink in.

"The third way is taken from possibility and necessity. We find in nature things which are possible to be or not to be. But it is . . . ''

"I am sorry, sir," I interrupted, "I don't understand that "to be or not to be'?''

"Well, take a plant for example. It can be alive or dead. It can be blooming, existing in all its beauty; or it can have disappeared, be part of the soil again.

"So we find that things are possible to be or not to be. But it is impossible for things to always exist, for if a thing can not-be at some time, there is a time when it does not exist. Therefore, if everything can not-be, then at one time there was nothing in existence. Now if this were true, then even now there would be nothing in existence, because that which does not exist begins to exist only through something already in existence.''

"If at one time nothing was in existence, it would have been impossible for anything to have begun to exist. Therefore, there must exist something, the existence of which is necessary, something that has its own necessity, does not receive it from anything else but, rather, giving it to everything else. This all men speak of as God.''

"Thank you, Father Thomas," the Mentor said.

"This is the argument from the first cause, isn't it?" I asked.

"Yes, it is," the Mentor replied.

"So what you are saying, Father Thomas, is that everything we know is caused by something else. If we go back through a succession of causes we must find something which was not caused by something else.''

44

"Precisely," St. Thomas agreed.

"Before you go on," the Mentor broke in, "listen to a different opinion. I would like you to meet a most delightful gentleman who was born in 1711. He was not only an excellent writer but one of the most significant philosophers."

The Mentor pointed to the seat beside me and in it sat a rather rotund, jovial man, wearing an embroidered frock and a short white wig.

"Mr. Penter, please meet David Hume," the Mentor said.

"Very pleased to meet you," Hume said.

"You are English I take it," I remarked.

"I beg your pardon, sir, I am Scottish," Hume said, clearly offended.

"My apologies," I mumbled.

"Mr. Hume," the Mentor continued, "in one of your books, *Dialogues Concerning Natural Religion,* you came up with some objections to Father Thomas' argument. Could you tell Mr. Penter about it?"

"Certainly," Hume said and turned toward me. "I raised three objections, as I recall. The first one was that the term 'necessary existence' has no meaning." He turned to St. Thomas: "You will forgive me for being so blunt, Father Thomas?"

"Quite alright, my son, I am used to arguments," St. Thomas replied.

Hume bowed slightly and turned back toward me. "Father Thomas contends that the Deity is a being 'necessarily existent' and he explains this by asserting that we must perceive it to be impossible not to exist. I contend that, as long as our faculties remain unchanged, this can never happen. For example, isn't it possible for us to conceive the non-existence of something we formerly thought of as existing? And also: why should it be necessary for our minds to suppose that any object remains always in being? I am afraid the term 'necessary existence' has no meaning."

Both St. Thomas and I started talking at the same time.

"Gentlemen," the Mentor said, raising his hand, "let Mr. Hume finish."

"The second objection concerns the succession of objects," Hume went on. "Each object is finite, limited. How can you ever prove the existence of something infinite by a succession of finite objects?

"The third objection concerns the cause of each individual object versus the cause of the whole. If we have twenty individual parts and I carefully explain to you the cause of each of the parts, have I explained to you the cause of the group of parts as a whole?"

I waited for St. Thomas to reply first but he seemed deeply absorbed in thought.

"Gentlemen," I said after a while, "it seems to me that all of the proofs I have heard so far are so abstract that they are only convincing to someone who already believes in God; it seems to depend so much on interpretation of language. Let me ask you this: was there ever an unbeliever who convinced himself by such an argument that God must exist?"

"Yes." The voice had come from behind my chair. I turned around, somewhat annoyed at the interruption. An older gentleman I had seen somewhere before stood there.

"I take it you feel you can make a contribution," I said.

"I believe I can."

"What is your name?"

"Mortimer Adler."

Now I remembered where I had seen him before. He was a philosopher and chairman of the board of editors of the *Encyclopedia Britannica.*

"Won't you take a seat, Mr. Adler?" the Mentor said.

Adler sat down and we all looked at him with expectation.

"First of all I agree with you, Mr. Penter. After the ninth century all philosophical thinking about God was influenced by faith."

"Are you rejecting the proofs we have been talking about then?" I asked.

"Yes."

"All of them?"

"Yes, all of them."

"I have the strange suspicion, Mr. Adler, that you are going to present a proof of your own."

"I am. But let me first get rid of some wrong ideas. The notion of God is not an empirical concept, it is a theoretical construct. God is beyond ordinary experience. Now there is nothing wrong with theoretical constructs, we use them all the time in theoretical physics. For example, we have never seen a meson or a black hole. We have created theoretical constructs about them because they explain what otherwise could not be explained—they are indispensable for their explanation. That is why I can come up with a new argument in the 20th century which was not possible in earlier centuries. The concept of theoretical constructs was simply not known before."

"Now my argument cannot provide certainty. It does not go beyond any doubt, just beyond a reasonable doubt. Please keep that in mind."

Hume wanted to object but the Mentor motioned him to be quiet.

"The difficulty in finding a proof is to ask the right question. And there is only one right question: why is there something rather than nothing?"

Adler looked at me, paused for a few seconds and then proceeded.

"Modern science has taught us that this world, in fact the entire cosmos, could have evolved differently. There

47

are many different universes possible or could have been possible and what could have been different is also capable of not existing at all. And here comes the tenuous part of the argument: that means that, at this very moment something is preventing our universe from being reduced to nothingness. Thus an act of God is required to preserve its existence.''

"Are you saying that this argument, and this argument alone has convinced you of the existence of God?'' I asked.

"Yes.''

"You were not a Christian or Jew or Moslem before you came up with your argument?''

"No, nor am I now. You see, to infer a benevolent, moral or personal God requires a leap of faith. There is no rational ground to cross that bridge.''

"So the question is: how meaningful is your proof?''

"That's a legitimate question,'' answered Adler without any sign of annoyance. "I believe that it produces a shell into which faith can be poured. That shell doesn't give any direction for your life, but without that shell faith is without foundation.''

I grabbed the Mentor by the arm and motioned him to step aside with me. "Somehow,'' I said, "this whole philosophical approach doesn't seem to work for me.''

The three philosophers started a heated debate.

"They build these large thought constructions,'' I continued, "on practically no facts at all. And the conclusions turn out to be of value only until someone else comes up with a different argument.''

The Mentor didn't say anything, but looked at me in a fatherly way.

"Tell me, even if I am convinced by any of these arguments, what am I supposed to do with an abstract concept of God that has nothing to do with the God that I was taught to believe in?''

The Mentor smiled and put his hand on my shoulder. "I told you it wouldn't be easy." He motioned me to walk down the aisle. I looked back at St. Thomas, Hume and Adler. They were absorbed in their debate and didn't notice our departure.

*   *   *

"We have one more proof to go, and this one is different," the Mentor said while we were walking down the stairs. "Over the centuries the proofs you have heard have influenced only philosophers and theologians. This third argument, though, has managed to convince many people."

We walked out into the garden of the library. On a bench sat a white-haired Anglican minister.

"This is William Paley," the Mentor said. Paley got up, shook hands and we all sat down.

"Mr. Paley was born in 1743 in England. He taught at Cambridge and later wrote several very influential books. But he is most remembered for his 'watch argument'. Mr. Paley, would you be so good as to relate your watch argument to Mr. Penter?"

"With pleasure. Suppose I crossed a meadow and hit my foot against a stone and were asked how the stone came to be there. I would answer that, for anything I knew to the contrary, it had lain there forever. But suppose I found a watch on the ground and someone asked me how the watch happened to be in that place, I should hardly think of the answer I gave before, that for anything I knew the watch had always been there. And that is because, when we come to inspect the watch we find that its several parts are framed and put together for a purpose, that they are so formed and adjusted as to produce motion, to tell the time of the day; that, if the different parts had been differently shaped or put together in a different way, either no motion at all would result or none that would serve any use.

"We draw the conclusion from this observation that the watch must have had a maker, that there must have existed at some time and some place an artificer or perhaps several artificers who formed the watch for a purpose.

"Now it would not weaken my conclusion if I had never seen a watch made before and if I had never known a watchmaker before, would it? Nor would it invalidate my conclusion if the watch were not perfect, if it sometimes went wrong or if it seldom went exactly right, would it?

"Nor would it bring any uncertainty to the argument if there were a few parts in the watch which I had never seen before and did not understand.

"And even if I had come to the conclusion that the watch's mechanism merely followed the laws of metals, I would have to believe that there was a maker.

"Now every manifestation of design which existed in the watch exists in the works of nature; with the difference, on the side of nature, of being greater and in a degree which exceeds all computation. I mean that the contrivances of nature surpass the contrivances of art, in the complexity, subtlety and curiosity of the mechanism; and still more, if possible, do they go beyond them in number and variety, yet in a multitude of cases are not less mechanical, not less evidently accommodated to their end, or suited to their purpose than are the most perfect productions of human ingenuity."

A butterfly alighted on Paley's sleeve, folding and opening its wings.

The Mentor got up and thanked Paley. Reluctantly I followed suit.

We walked toward the gate. "Now you are going to tell me that there is a counterargument to that too, aren't you?" I said.

"I'm afraid so," said the Mentor.

"Evolution?"

"Among other things."

The Mentor pointed to a building across from the library, the large lecture hall. "I shall leave you here, my friend. Good luck."

I shook his hand and thanked him. "You must tell me your name," I said.

"It doesn't matter."

3
The Universe

The large lecture hall was filled to capacity. A giant screen covered the front.

A distinguished looking older gentleman stood up from the front row and surveyed the audience. The voices died down almost immediately.

"Ladies and gentlemen. I have been asked to act as moderator for this meeting. Today's presentations are intended to answer the questions: What do we know about life? Where did we come from? What do we know about the development and, perhaps, the origin of the universe and of life on earth?

"The presentation this morning will be given by an astronomer, the talk this afternoon by a biologist."

The moderator sat down. A man, just short of 40, with a beard and glasses, walked up to the screen.

"Ladies and gentlemen. In ancient times it was believed that the sky was suspended above a flat earth and that it contained water which occasionally came down to us as rain. It was believed that the stars and the sun were relatively small objects, moved across the sky by the gods or by a god and that both earth and sky were only a few thousand years old."

53

The lecture hall darkened and an ancient drawing of earth and heaven appeared on the screen.

"Between three and two thousand BC the science of astronomy begins. The oldest evidence we have is that of astronomical stations in Egypt, Babylonia, Greece and China, set up to record the position of the sun and the moon, and later of some of the brighter stars. They detect regularities, cycles. These ancient people realize that it takes some 360 days for the sun to come back to the same position and for the seasons to repeat themselves. They discover that the moon during this annual cycle repeats its own position 12 times. Although these numbers turn out to be inaccurate later on, they form the basis for the 12 month year and the 360 degree circle.

"These ancient people believed that the sun is transported during the night along the horizon so that it can reappear on the opposite side in the morning. Then in approximately 580 BC Anaximander in Greece comes up with the notion that the earth might not be flat, but a cylinder, with the sun, the moon and the stars rotating around the earth.

"Around 500 BC Parmenides, a pupil of Pythagoras, first suggests that the earth might be a sphere. This theory was not widely accepted until Aristotle, around 350 BC noticed that, during a lunar eclipse, the earth's own shadow on the moon was round."

The image on the screen, which had shown various scenes of ancient Greece and then the head of Aristotle, now changed to a drawing of concentric spheres.

"With the earth recognized as a sphere and the planets and stars to be the same, several Greek astronomers in succession came up with explanations for a planetary system, culminating in the system of Ptolemy in the second century AD. Ptolemy's system was an intricate, well thought-out scheme of planetary motion. Since the telescope had not been invented yet and the measurements were quite inaccurate, this scheme explained the appearance and positions of planets and stars reasonably well, even though it still assumed the earth to be at the center of the universe.

"Gradually, no longer able to defend the flat earth and suspended sky of the Old Testament, the Christian church adopted Ptolemy's system. Peter Lombard and Thomas Aquinas contributed greatly to what was now called the 'sacred theory of the universe' and it is this system that Dante expresses in his works.

"In this view of the universe the earth is surrounded by successive transparent spheres or heavens, rotated by angels, each sphere containing one or more of the heavenly bodies in it. The one nearest to the earth carries the moon. The next, Mercury; the next, Venus; the next, the sun; the next three Mars, Jupiter and Saturn. The eighth sphere carries the fixed stars; the ninth the mobile stars. And enclosing all is the tenth heaven. And here, in a light which no-one can enter, God sits enthroned.

"In attendance of God were a vast host of angels, who were divided into three hierarchies: one serving God in the tenth heaven, one serving in the heavens from one to nine, and one on earth.

"In the innards of the earth was hell. It was occupied by Lucifer and his fallen angels, also referred to as devils or demons. Of these fallen angels some were able to move through the heavens and on earth, giving trouble to the good angels and causing lightning, storms, hail or drought."

Now the face of a man appeared on the screen.

"By the year 1500 science had developed to the point where measurements of the position of the planets and the moon could be made with greater accuracy. And now it became obvious that there was something wrong with the Ptolemaic system. It was this man, Nikolai Kopernik, better known as Nicolaus Copernicus, a native of Poland, who, following an earlier Greek idea, came up with a better explanation of the planetary system: the sun is at the center, the planets, including the earth, rotate around it, the moon circles the earth and the earth spins about its own axis.

"Copernicus' theory was proven by Galileo Galilei, a professor of mechanics, geometry and astronomy at the universities of Florence, Pisa and Padua. By 1613, having built one of the first telescopes, he convinced himself from his observations that Copernicus' theory was indeed correct.

"In the meantime his contemporary, Johannes Kepler in Germany, had taken Copernicus' theory and calculated the orbits of the planets more exactly. He found that these orbits were not spherical, but elliptical."

The image on the screen had changed from the face of Copernicus to Galileo and then Kepler. Now it showed Isaac Newton.

"Some 70 years later Isaac Newton discovered the law of gravitation and the mathematical relationship between the size of a planet, its distance from the sun and its orbital speed. The theory of the solar system now had its solid mathematical foundation.

"With the telescope and better mathematics the discovery of the universe now gained speed. In 1781 William Herschel discovered Uranus, the seventh planet in the solar system. Mapping the orbit of Uranus after its discovery he noted a slight irregularity. Calculations showed that there must be yet another planet outside the orbit of Uranus. This eighth planet, Neptune, was discovered in 1846. And, again, from minute irregularities in Neptune's orbit it was suspected that there was a ninth planet. This last planet—for now—Pluto, was first seen in 1930."

Having shown the various planets, the screen now suddenly displayed a vast cloud of stars.

56

"At first it was assumed that our solar system was at the center of the universe, since the night sky is filled with roughly an equal number of stars in all directions. Immanuel Kant then observed the luminous cloud with spiral arms in Andromeda and proposed that it might be another galaxy of stars.

"In 1915 Harlow Shapley, making measurements at the Mt. Wilson observatory in California, realized that our 'Milky Way' galaxy is slowly rotating, has spiral arms just like the Andromeda galaxy and that our sun and its planets are not located in its center, but two-thirds toward the edge in one of the spiral arms. Only nine years later, in 1924, Edwin Hubble, again at Mt. Wilson observatory, discovered that there are many other galaxies."

The screen showed a number of colorful cloud-like galaxies with an immense number of stars in the foreground. Suddenly the face of Einstein appeared.

"Momentous as these discoveries were, nothing produced as large an impact on astronomy as the mathematics of Albert Einstein. He presented his general theory of relativity in 1916 and within a very short time a large number of important facts about the universe became clear. In 1930 Edwin Hubble discovered that the universe is expanding. And in 1939 Hans Bethe discovered that nuclear fusion creates the light of the stars.

"Let me now give you a brief summary of what we know about the universe and its origin.

"Some 15 to 20 billion years ago everything we see today started in an explosion of incredible magnitude. After the first second of this gigantic fireball the temperature of it was some 9 billion degrees Fahrenheit. Only hydrogen and helium, the two lightest elements, were present. The fireball expanded and cooled; after 100,000 years the temperature was 18,000 degrees Fahrenheit.

"The gases, hydrogen and helium, continued expanding outward and cooling off. A billion years or so later all light disappeared; the universe was in complete darkness. Now the gas was sufficiently cool to condense into galaxies by the force of gravity and, from that point into individual stars.

"If a gas cloud is pulled together by the attraction of the individual atoms, the interior of the cloud heats up. The more compressed the interior becomes, the higher the temperature. If the mass of the gas cloud is sufficient, the temperature in the center of a ball of gas can reach 7 billion degrees Fahrenheit. At this temperature a new phenomenon appears: nuclear fusion. It converts hydrogen into helium and by doing so releases a tremendous amount of energy in the form of heat, light and other radiation. This is the reason why stars are so bright; stars are slowly burning nuclear furnaces.

"Our sun is such a nuclear furnace, converting hydrogen into helium. It is a relatively new star; it didn't begin to exist until some 5 billion years ago.

"Gas clouds still exist today in the universe and new stars are still being formed. Our galaxy contains some 400 billion stars, many much larger than our sun. There are some 100 billion galaxies in the observable universe."

The Astronomer paused and let the screen tell the story. Brilliant pictures of stars, star clusters and vast galaxies appeared in succession.

"If the original gas cloud is large, it forms a large star and the pressure in its interior is higher. This causes the star to convert hydrogen into helium faster, the star is brighter, but its life is shorter, perhaps only a few million years. A small star, such as our sun, is dimmer but lasts a few billion years.

"Once a star has burned up its hydrogen fuel it swells to a hundred times its size and its surface temperature drops to half. At this stage it is called a red giant. It will happen to our sun in about 6 billion years. As a red giant the sun will have a size larger than the orbit of Mercury; it

58

will singe the surface of the earth and all life here will cease.

"How long a star will last in this stage depends on its size. A relatively small star like the sun will begin to shrink into a white dwarf after about 100 million years. This will be the end of its life, an incredible dense ball only one millionth its former size, cooling off until it no longer emits any light.

"A larger star, however, will continue in a sequence of nuclear fusions, producing the heavier elements: carbon, oxygen, neon, magnesium, silicon, sulfur, iron. When it reaches iron, it too will collapse. But then, rather than cool off as a white dwarf, it explodes with a bright flash, and at that moment forms elements heavier than iron, for example gold, platinum and silver. Such a 'supernova' explosion sends the elements off into space in a gigantic burst of gas clouds. It is from such a cloud of an ancient supernova that our sun, the earth and the other planets were formed. The cloud drifted through space, cooled off and condensed again into stars and planets. The presence of the heavier elements makes it certain that our solar system was once part of an exploding star."

The screen now showed a colorful picture of a nebula.

"This is where we came from, ladies and gentlemen. You and I, every atom in our bodies, every animal, every plant, and every stone on this earth was once, billions of years ago, part of a gas cloud in space, expelled from a massive exploding star.

"When the earth formed, its interior heated up again through the pressure of gravity, aided by the decay of radioactive material in its core. Since the earth is much smaller than the sun, its temperature is much lower. Nevertheless, the earth has a molten core.

"Some 4.6 billion years ago at its beginning, the earth was a naked body of rock without air or water. The molten core expanded and some of its material was pushed to the surface in volcanoes. The lava from these volcanoes carried with it many of the elements stored inside the earth from the original cloud, most importantly hydrogen, water vapor, methane, ammonia and nitrogen. These gasses formed the primitive atmosphere, an atmosphere we could not live in today because it contained almost no free oxygen."

The image on the screen showed a desolate early earth.

"This is how we have to imagine our earth a few hundred million years after its formation. A small, dark sphere of rock, circling a relatively small star together with other planets, four of which are far larger than the earth.

"Yes, ladies and gentlemen, we are standing on an insignificant little ball in the universe. If a traveller from outer space were to observe our solar system from a distance even closer than the distance of the nearest other star he would probably say that our sun was a dim star circled by four planets and some debris!

"Let me give you an idea of size. If you imagine the sun to be a ball 5 inches in diameter, which means a reduction by a factor of 10 billion, then the earth is 60 feet away and is a mere speck of dust. On this scale the nearest other star, Alpha Centauri, is 2000 miles away.

"It takes light roughly one second to travel from the moon to the earth and 8 minutes from the sun to the earth. Alpha Centauri is more than 4 light years away. We are some 40,000 light years from the center of our galaxy and the nearest other galaxy is 2 million light years away; the most distant galaxies have a distance of some 15 billion light years.

"Thank you, ladies and gentlemen," the Astronomer said.

The lights came on and the lecture hall stirred.

"Sir," a dark-haired young man in the third row said

immediately, "you never once mentioned God. Where does he come in?"

The Astronomer looked at the young man for a while and then said, "I can't answer that question."

The young man shook his head. "I am not going to let you get away with this, sir. Assuming that what you have presented is true, that the universe was a fireball 15 billion years ago and we can explain everything since then in purely physical terms, doesn't that still leave the question: who created the fireball? Who created matter and energy?"

"Yes, it does, and I don't have an answer for it," replied the Astronomer.

"Sir, do you believe in God?" the young man asked.

The Astronomer stared at the floor for a long time and then said quietly: "I am not sure."

The moderator got up and said: "I don't think there is any need to bring up one's personal beliefs here."

"It's alright," the Astronomer broke in. "Let me explain. I realize that, despite all the progress we have made in science we cannot explain the cause of the primordial explosion. The energy and matter must have come from somewhere but, it seems, all the evidence of what existed before was destroyed in the explosion.

"My main problem is with what our religions, especially Judaism and Christianity believe that God has done. If I accept the Bible as the word of God, I am instantly troubled by many questions. Why would God single out this insignificant planet? If God made man the center of creation, why would he create the universe and then wait 15 billion years to create man? And why would he create man several million years ago, but not contact him until 3500 years ago? And why does this contact coincide with the start of writing?

"And why is there all this violence in the universe? It's

a ghastly place with exploding stars, deadly radiation and violent destruction. Why would God create such a place?

"And why is the story of creation so wrong in Genesis of the Old Testament? Earth is there first, already containing air and water, then light is created and after this the stars. Why would God give this reversed story to Moses, to his chosen people, when at that time other civilizations already had a much better knowledge of the universe? And why is the story in Genesis so much like one an ancient, ignorant man would imagine the universe to be?"

The young man sat down. Another hand went up.

"But we have to assume," a woman said, "that God can do anything he wants to. He is almighty. He could even have created the universe yesterday and make us believe it happened 15 billion years ago."

The Astronomer shook his head violently. "That's a cop-out. If you are thinking this way you are cutting yourself off from reason. Ask yourself this: which should I believe, that which I and many other people observe supported by many other facts that fit into a system of science without any contradictions; or that which some people believe without any supporting facts at all?"

A number of hands had risen but the moderator called a lunch recess.

*   *   *

I went to the cafeteria on the lower floor, bought a sandwich and sat down at a table.

I didn't quite agree with what the Astronomer had said about the reasons for doubting the existence of God. It seemed to me that a sharp distinction needed to be made between religious doctrine and the real question of God's existence. The vast and awesome cosmos he had shown seemed to indicate that the universe was indeed the work of God. I wondered what other scientists thought about this question.

"May I join you?" said a voice.

I nearly choked on my sandwich when I looked up. There was Albert Einstein, with his rumpled sweater, drooping moustache and white hair flying in all directions. Dumbfounded, with my mouth full, I waved for him to sit down.

He looked at me without saying anything and I finally managed to swallow.

"Professor Einstein, may I ask you a question?"

"But of course," he answered in a heavy German accent, smiling.

"Did you believe in God?"

"Yes, I did."

"You were . . . Jewish?"

He shook his head slowly. "By ancestry only. I didn't believe in a personal God, that is a God who influences the lives of people or who can be influenced by people through prayer. So I didn't go along with either Judaism or Christianity or any of the traditional religions."

"What did you believe in then?" I asked.

"Let me explain it this way: I think everyone who is seriously involved in the pursuit of science becomes convinced that a spirit is manifest in the laws of the universe—a spirit vastly superior to that of man. It is a kind of cosmic religious feeling. It is a deep conviction of the rationality of the universe. I think in this materialistic world of ours, scientists may be the only profoundly religious people."

"Did you believe in an immortal soul?"

"No."

"Do you conceive God as being omnipotent?"

"Ah, there is a serious flaw here in the teachings of both Judaism and Christianity. If you say that God is omnipotent, has created everything, yet rewards and punishes us, he would be passing judgment on himself, wouldn't he?"

I had never thought about that.

"You say what really gives you this religious feeling is the rationality of the laws of the universe. Does nature have a purpose?"

"No, no purpose or goal. What I see in nature is a magnificent structure which we can comprehend only imperfectly and which should fill every thinking person with humility. But our existence acquires meaning only by setting goals ourselves."

"What do you feel about religious organizations?"

"Well, I think they should give up their doctrines of a personal God and concentrate on their real mission: teaching moral values. You see, there is nothing divine about morality; it is a purely human affair."

"But despite the fact that you didn't accept any religious doctrine, you believed in the existence of God?"

"Yes, I did."

As I was thinking of the next question I noticed that Einstein was not wearing socks. "So it's true, Professor, you do not wear socks."

"Oh, that," Einstein replied with a loud, hearty laugh, "yes, you see, the big toe always makes a hole in the sock, so I stopped wearing them altogether."

I looked at the kindly old man. "May I ask you something that I have been curious about for a long time?"

"Certainly."

"Your controversy with Niels Bohr. As I understand it you did not agree with his idea that individual atoms are governed by chance only rather than strict physical laws."

"Yes, if you look at it from the point of view of God, why would he create such an untidy universe?"

"And you said: God does not throw dice."

Einstein smiled into the empty space and said: *"Ja, Gott würfelt nicht."*

"And mainly because of your belief in the existence of God you refused to accept a chance or statistical approach to the universe?"

Einstein nodded.

"Even though almost all other scientists had accepted it?"

Einstein nodded again.

"And you spent the last 40 years of your life searching for a unified-field theory that would prove that the statistical approach was wrong."

"Yes."

"Did you ever find it?"

Einstein looked at me with his large eyes and shook his head slowly. "No, I never did."

I shook his hand and thanked him. As I walked out I turned around. He was still sitting at the table, a sad old man who had made one of the greatest discoveries in science, yet hadn't found what he was looking for.

*   *   *

I went upstairs to the lecture hall and took my seat. After a few minutes the moderator brought the meeting to order and a serious gentleman in an ill-fitting suit walked to the front of the screen.

"Ladies and gentlemen," the Biologist began, "I would like to first give you the background of how we came to our knowledge about the beginning of life. In the Jewish and Christian world the Old Testament was the dominant factor for a long time. There are two somewhat conflicting accounts on the creation of life in Genesis. The first one says that God created grass, herbs and trees on the third day, 'moving creatures' and fowl on the fifth day, and cattle, 'creeping things', beast and man, both male and female, on the sixth day.

"The second account states that God created man

first. Then, out of earth, he created 'every beast and fowl and brought them to Adam to name them,' after which he formed Eve out of Adam's rib.

"The Greeks made a small amount of progress in the life sciences, but when Christianity became dominant in the western world, all progress in this field stopped. The Church considered any effort to explore life futile and dangerous. Anyone who would dare to experiment with chemicals or dissect a body was considered the devil's disciple. Chemistry was black magic and sorcery. In 1163 Pope Alexander forbade the study of physics and the 'laws of the world.' For more than 1600 years after the beginning of Christianity scientific progress was at a standstill.

"The age of the earth and of life was treated in the same way. The Bible gives a chronology of ancestors and of their ages back to Adam. From this information the theologians calculated the age of the world. In 1640 Pope Gregory VIII officially approved the view that the world was created in 5199 BC, while the English church under Archbishop Ussher put this date at 4004 BC.

"But beginning around 1590 these dates and the literal interpretation of the Bible started to become a problem. Fossils of animals and plants were discovered in increasing numbers in the ground. These were puzzling, since it was believed that the earth had not changed since creation. At first an explanation was found which said that the animals and plants had been buried in the silt during the flood.

"But then Egyptian monuments and records were discovered which were apparently of very old age. They indicated in their own chronology that their civilization had already been in existence before 5199 BC and that there had been no interruption by a flood.

"From this point on, progress in the life sciences became more visible. In 1661 Robert Boyle attacked the widely held view developed by the Greeks that the four fundamental elements were earth, air, fire and water.

66

Instead he developed the concept of particles; and in rapid succession more and more of the substances known to man were broken down into far more fundamental elements.

"At the same time an increasing number of species of plants and animals were continually being discovered. By 1750 more than 4000 different species were known. And with the construction of the first microscope in 1674 by Van Leeuwenhoek a whole new area of life opened up.

"In 1803 Dalton renewed and elaborated the idea of atomic elements, proposed more than 2000 years earlier by some of the Greek philosophers. In 1807 Berzelius separated chemistry into organic and inorganic, where all organic compounds come from living things. In 1820 Braconnot isolated the first amino acid, the basic building block of proteins. In 1849 Liebig realized the overwhelming importance and universality of proteins for life.

"On a different front, in 1856, at Neanderthal in Germany, a human skull was unearthed which had a very primitive, apelike appearance, suggesting a slow development of man from the ape. And in 1858 the theory of evolution by Charles Darwin and Alfred Russel Wallace exploded like a bombshell. It showed, with considerable evidence, that man had developed from lower animals.

"This fueled further discoveries in the chemistry of life. It was found that, although there is a very large variety of proteins, the proteins of all living things consist of a relatively small variety of nucleic acid molecules. For the first time organic compounds could be made in the laboratory from inorganic ones. In 1869 T. H. Huxley proposed that life could have arisen from inorganic chemicals.

"But the most important breakthorough toward a glimpse of the origin of life has come only very recently. In 1952 Miller and Urey at the University of Chicago simulated the atmosphere of the primitive earth in a flask:

water vapor, ammonia, methane and hydrogen. When they passed a spark through this mixture they were able to produce amino acids. Calvin at Berkeley repeated the experiment using electron bombardment instead of the spark and Sagan at Cornell used ultraviolet light. It was found that amino acids form the basis for DNA, the molecule responsible for reproduction of life. In 1953 Watson and Crick at Cambridge identified the double helix structure of DNA. Since then it has been found that organic matter is in fact abundant in the universe, it has been found even in interstellar gas. Amino acids have been found in meteorites. And scientists have caused short nucleic acids to duplicate their molecular structure."

The Biologist paused. Dozens of slides had been shown on the screen; now the lights came on.

"With this knowledge, so recently acquired," he continued, "it is now possible to put together a picture of how life began on this earth and how it developed into man. I hasten to add that this is a very preliminary picture, that our knowledge is as yet far too small for this picture to be complete. But it is our best knowledge, far better than anything we have ever had before, and fitting well into every other known fact.

"How did life on earth begin? As we have heard, the atmosphere on the surface of the earth some 4.6 billion years ago consisted of water vapor, methane, ammonia and hydrogen. Most of the surface was covered by water; the temperature was somewhat higher than it is today. There was a great deal of volcanic activity, thunderstorm, lightning and a rather high level of nuclear and ultraviolet radiation. We now know that under these conditions amino acids form rather easily.

"Simple organic compounds assembled into more complex molecules with inorganic material acting as a catalyst. Under this condition a molecule can grow by using other molecules as nutrients, and here the first competition for food began. A large variety of such complex molecules were formed, many died from lack of food and some were consumed by others.

"At this point some of the assemblies of amino acids exhibit a property which makes their kind particularly well suited for survival: they can split in half, each half absorbing other molecules and thus doubling their number. This replication was the first sign of life.

"After this the first cells appeared, self-contained organisms with a number of highly complex molecules, capable of self-replication and growth through the absorption of food molecules. This happened some 3 or 4 billion years ago. Since at that time radiation levels were still very high, life only existed in the water.

"Cells then combined themselves into a bewildering variety. Some combinations of cells were better able to compete for the food and thus grew in number; the others died or were absorbed. For a long time the blue-green algae was the most successful lifeform on earth. It dominated life in the water. Being a plant, it could produce food from sunlight and in doing so also produce oxygen. The oxygen slowly accumulated in the atmosphere and created the ozone layer which now shields the earth from radiation. Thus protected, plants started growing on land.

"Some 600 million years ago the dominance of the blue-green algae was suddenly broken. Other, more complex lifeforms developed rapidly. The first trilobites appeared, small animals a little larger than an insect.

"About 400 million years ago the first fish appeared. About the same time or shortly thereafter the atmosphere had enough oxygen to support animal life on land. Life probably moved onto land because it got too crowded in the water.

"Again we find the same evolutionary mechanism as in the molecules. That organism most suited for the environment survives and thrives. The reproduction of a living organism is not perfect, occasionally it produces variations, mutations. If the mutation gives the organism an advantage in the competition for food, it will survive better and eventually dominate, producing an improvement in the species or, though rarely, a new species. If the mutation produces a disadvantage, the organism dies out.

"Evolution on land started with amphibians and insects. Plants, already abundant, provided food for the animals. Reptiles appeared some 350 million years ago, and from these evolved mammals about 200 million years ago and then within the mammals the primates 70 million years ago. Man is one of the branches of the primates and became a separate species only about 3 million years ago.

"Man is the most successful of the species because of his brain. Considering body weight, man's brain is larger than that of any other animal and it also has a more refined structure.

"It is important to realize that man's brain is actually three brains in one. The innermost brain is located directly at the top of the spinal cord. It controls reproduction, self-preservation, heartbeat, blood circulation and respiration. This part of the brain we inherited from the fish, amphibian and reptile. It is the seat of aggression and ritual behavior.

"Surrounding this part of the brain is the so-called limbic system, which we inherited from the mammalian stage in the evolution. This part of the brain controls our moods and emotions and the concern and care for the young. Both the innermost brain and the limbic system are largely pre-programmed at birth, its behavior not learned, but what we commonly call instinct.

"The outermost layer of the human brain is called the neocortex. This part is absent in lower animals. It can be found in apes, whales and especially dolphins, but to a much smaller extent.

70

"At birth the neocortex is smooth. As the baby learns, especially during the first five years of its life, the surface of the neocortex becomes more and more wrinkled. The size of the human brain seems to have very little to do with intelligence; however the complexity of the surface of the neocortex does.

"This neocortex, which comprises two thirds of the brain in man, stores learned information. It is the seat of intuition and critical analysis. Here ideas and inspirations are formed; it is the seat of consciousness. It is the neocortex which gives man a large, albeit somewhat unreliable memory, and allows him to form complex languages and writing, and through writing to store a vast amount of information outside his brain in books and libraries."

The Biologist sat down. The lecture hall was quiet.

A man in the front row raised his hand and asked: "In all of these findings from the early atmosphere to man, is there any evidence that God lent a helping hand?"

The moderator squirmed uncomfortably but accepted the inevitable.

The Biologist shook his head. "We now have, for the first time in human history, a reasonable explanation for the entire existence of life without having to resort to the existence of God."

"Lies!" The voice had come from the back of the lecture hall and all heads turned toward it.

"Lies, all of it!" The voice belonged to a balding man, about 50 years old, with rimless glasses.

The moderator stood up. "Would you identify yourself, please?"

"I am Dr. Henry Morris from the Christian Heritage College in San Diego."

"Oh, yes," the Biologist said, "the creationist."

"Please feel free to speak," the chairman said.

"You so-called scientists are so quick to get rid of God," Dr. Morris said. "An overwhelming body of evidence proves that the earth and its life were created about 6000 to 10,000 years ago, in six days, by forces which are no longer in operation, and that a flood some time after that innundated the entire surface of the earth.

"First, the age of the world. The earth is claimed to be 4.6 billion years old as measured by radioactive dating. I say this is totally, inexcusably wrong. In radioactive dating one has to make such wild assumptions as to render the whole thing ridiculously inaccurate. Just by changing the assumptions a little I can make the results change from billions of years to thousands of years.

"Second, it is simply too fantastic to assume that such complex organisms evolved by chance alone. Life could never have created itself. Fossil records show that a much greater variety of species existed in the past compared to now. This clearly indicates that the species were created all at once and then gradually died out.

"Third, the fossil records themselves. I am convinced that they are the result of animals and plants killed in the great flood and buried in the silt. Why is it that we have never found any fossils linking the species? I'll tell you why: because evolution never took place!

"Fourth, the first law of thermodynamics tells us that energy cannot be created or destroyed, it always remains constant. This first law of thermodynamics alone tells us that the universe could not have created itself; there must have been some supernatural force at work.

"And fifth and most important: the second law of thermodynamics. This law states that all energy evens out with time, that every system moves from organization toward disorganization. For example, if, initially, all the heat is concentrated in one point in the system it will, with time, flow to the other parts of the system until, eventually, the entire system is at the same uniform low temperature. It also says that if I build a house it will, with time, decay until there is nothing but a uniform layer of rubble on the ground. But what you are claiming is that life, without any outside help, grew more and more complex, fantastically complex as a matter of fact. This, I maintain, violates the second law of thermodynamics and, therefore, is only conceivable with the help of God."

"Dr. Morris," the Biologist said calmly, "you are a fundamentalist, are you not?"

"My religious convictions have nothing to do with the scientific statements I just made, sir," Dr. Morris answered.

"Oh, but they do, Dr. Morris," the Biologist insisted, still in a very calm voice, "they do indeed, or how could you ever come to the conclusion that the world was created in six days?

"Your approach to science, Dr. Morris, I would call selective ignorance. You accept what supports the Bible and reject what does not, ignoring a great deal of inconvenient evidence in the process.

"You made five points, let me answer them. First radioactive dating. You are totally wrong about its accuracy. It has been cross-checked in many, many different ways. Even the worst method of radioactive dating gives an inaccuracy of only a few percent.

"Your second point has a serious weakness. Even if, as you claim, we are way off in our absolute scale of radioactive dating, your theory is destroyed by the fact that fossils of simple lifeforms are always older than those of more complex ones.

"You say that it is simply unimaginable that life could have created itself. What you forget, Dr. Morris, is the time involved. Nobody can imagine 4.6 billion years or even 100 million years. A lot of different combinations of molecules and cells can form in such a long time. Time, Dr. Morris, that's the key!

"As to your third point, the missing links between the species, I am dissatisfied too, but not at all disturbed.

Your statement is not entirely true. We have found skulls of some ancestors of man which very clearly point toward a link with primates. Not the entire link yet, I agree, but give us time, we started investigating a little over 100 years ago what took billions of years to evolve.

"Development from one species to another is probably an unstable occurrence which happens only extremely rarely. Once a new species exists it lasts for a long time. The odds on skull or bone fossils being generated and surviving for a long time are extremely small, so that the chance of finding the fossils of a transition between species is miniscule. But, I think, with time and improved methods we might find a number of them.

"Your fourth point uses the first law of thermodynamics, the conservation of energy. On this we agree, Dr. Morris; the universe did not create itself, at least not by any of the physical laws we have discovered so far. But you, because you believe in the Bible, immediately say that it must have been God who created the universe. I, as a scientist, cannot say this, because I don't know that it is true. All I can say is that we don't know.

"Now to your last and what you call your most important argument, the second law of thermodynamics. You stated it correctly but you ignored one very important factor, one that should be known to every science major. While the energy of a system spreads out toward a uniform level with time, it can very easily peak in different parts of the system for a time. For example, if I give energy to a churchbell by pushing it hard, the clapper will strike the bell and emit periodic bursts of sound. Overall, the energy that I have supplied by pushing the bell is dying down all right, but it does so in bursts of gradually decreasing sound.

"Exactly the same situation occurs in the universe. The temperature was initially very hot and concentrated in a point. It gradually spread out and cooled down and does

74

so still today. But in spreading out clouds of gas contract and form local hot spots, the stars. Stars then cool down and eventually the entire universe will be at a uniform low temperature. But in the meantime the heat from our local hot spot, the sun, radiating onto the earth, is more than sufficient to account for all the energy required to assemble even the most complex lifeforms."

"You think you have all the answers," Dr. Morris replied. "I bet you have never even bothered to read the Bible."

"On the contrary, Dr. Morris," the Biologist said, "I have read the Bible. Many times, as a matter of fact. And the more I read it, the more I came to the conclusion that it is full of contradictions. Tell me, Dr. Morris, you believe that the Bible is true, don't you?"

"Yes, of course," said Dr. Morris.

"Every word of it?"

"Every word of it!"

"And that it is the word of God?"

"Yes," answered Dr. Morris.

"Then how do you explain," asked the Biologist, "that the Egyptians and Babylonians, long before the book of Moses, had very similar accounts of the creation, that, especially the Babylonian account even contains some of the similar names and that it even has the story of the flood. Were these stories inspired by God too, even though the Babylonians believed in many gods? How do you explain the fact that in Chapter 1 in Genesis God created man and woman together on the sixth day, after the animals, and in chapter 2 he creates first Adam, then the animals, and then Eve? One of those accounts must be untrue.

"I have always been amazed by the extremely detailed description of the flood in the Bible and these details have caused me some problems. For example, how did Noah get all the animals, two of every species, into an ark 450 by

75 by 45 feet? There are more than a million different species. And where did he store all the food for these animals for an entire year? It says that God told Noah to bring all these animals to the ark. How did he get the Kangaroo, which only lives in Australia? Or the Polar Bear? And how about all the microbes? And it says that there were three stories in the ark but only a single window, 18 inches square, on the top story, which was closed for more than 190 days. How did all these animals breathe?

"And how about the plants, how did they survive? God told Noah that he would destroy every living substance on the face of the earth. It says that the water was higher than the tallest mountain by 22 feet. How did plants survive under 29,000 feet of water for an entire year? Where do the plants we have now come from?

"And how do you account for the different races? If the story of the flood is true we are all descendants from Noah and his three sons. How could the different races have developed in such a short time?

"And lastly, why would a benevolent God kill almost all the animals just because he was angry with man?

"No, Dr. Morris, at least that portion of the Bible is not inspired by God; it is not a true story, but rather legend inherited from the Egyptians and Babylonians, changed to fit the Jewish religion, told and retold over generations and altered in the process and finally written down as the book of Moses. You may sincerely believe what you are saying, Dr. Morris, but if so, I feel sorry for you. You have been grossly misled by religious tradition."

The lecture hall became tumultuous. Dr. Morris protested but his voice was drowned out. The moderator got up and restored order. Several hands were up in the air.

The moderator pointed at someone in the front and said: "Would you identify yourself, please?"

A man of about 50 with a gap in his teeth stood up.

"My name is Alan Hayward. First let me put some distance between myself and Dr. Morris. Claims such as an age of the earth of 10,000 years or the flood are ridiculous. They do the Christian cause more harm than good."

Most of the audience applauded.

"But the theory of evolution has some serious problems. There seem to be so many unexplained gaps and inconsistencies. For example, how do you explain flight? If evolution is correct, then every development took place in small steps and every small step must have given an advantage to survival. But how did wings form? A partially developed wing is of no use to a bird or an insect, you can't fly with it. To fly, it must at the same time have a powerful muscle and a large, lightweight structure.

"Or take the case of the bombardier beetle. It has a kind of flame thrower in its body with which it can scorch its enemies. With its glands it manufactures two explosive chemicals, hydroquinine and hydrogen peroxide, stores them in two separate chambers and releases them into a sort of combustion chamber in the rear of its body. In the trial and error way of evolution such a species would have blown itself up very early in the development.

"Or in the case of one kind of sea slug. It eats a small animal called the Coelenterata which is covered with poisonous stings. Somehow the sea slug manages to swallow its prey with the stings coiled up and, therefore, harmless. In the stomach of the sea slug these stings work themselves through narrow tubes to the surface where they stick out and protect the sea slug. How could that have evolved without poisoning the sea slug in the course of the development?

To me the evolution of life is simply unimaginable without some guiding influence, without a superior intellect, without God!"

Hayward sat down.

"I don't have a simple explanation, Mr. Hayward," the Biologist said. "But you, too, forget time. Over the last billion years or so many, many different species evolved and an unimaginable number of variations appeared. Most of these variations disappeared almost immediately, perhaps because they stung themselves to death, exploded or killed themselves trying to fly. But a small percentage, a very small percentage made it all the way through despite the odds.

"I cannot agree with your conclusion. Our knowledge is like a giant puzzle where some pieces are still in a pile on the table but enough of them have been put together to show a distinct picture. At this point we are entitled to say: It is a house, not a ship. What you are saying is: a) because some of the pieces are missing we cannot draw any conclusions, and b) it is not a house, it is a tree—because someone has told you to expect a tree."

4
Miracles

I entered the skyscraper and looked up the floor number for the association on the direction board. After taking the elevator up to the twelfth floor and, having searched for a minute, I found the door with the sign: Investigative Committee, Session 9 am. Inside, a group of people were sitting around a conference table; the room was smoke-filled. I took a seat along the wall.

After a few minutes the committee chairman knocked a spoon against his coffee cup and said: "Let's get started, ladies and gentlemen. Who would like to lead off?"

One of the members raised his hand and said: "May I request that, for the duration of this meeting we refrain from smoking?"

There was some grumbling around the table.

"I second the motion," a woman said.

"I think we should respect the wish of our non-smokers," the chairman said, "especially since we are dealing with an explosive subject."

There was considerable booing. The smoking, however, stopped.

"Now, then, who wants to start, this time on the real subject?"

One of the members raised his hand. "I thought it

might be a good idea if we heard someone in defense of miracles first. One of the ablest defenses was, in my opinion, presented by C. S. Lewis. I have him waiting in the witness chamber. With your permission . . . ''

The other committee member nodded and C. S. Lewis was brought in. He took a seat at the head of the table.

"Mr. Lewis," the member said, "you were born in 1898 in Belfast, Northern Ireland, is that correct?"

"Correct," Lewis said.

"I believe you taught at Oxford and Cambridge and you wrote some 40 books. As a young man you were an atheist, were you not?"

"I was," said Lewis.

"But in 1929 you converted to Christianity and became one of its stoutest defenders. One of your books is entitled *Miracles* and since that is our subject today, I wonder if you might give us a summary of it."

"I'll be happy to," Lewis said. "First let me state that the question whether miracles occur cannot be answered simply by experience. Every event which we might claim to be a miracle is something presented to our senses, and our senses are not infallible. If anything extraordinary happens we can always dismiss it, saying that we were the victims of an illusion.

"And if immediate experience cannot prove or disprove a miracle, history can do even less for us. Only a philosophical inquiry can convince us: If we come to the conclusion that miracles are not intrinsically improbable, then the existing evidence will be sufficient to convince us that quite a number of miracles have occurred. Thus our task is to prove that miracles are not intrinsically improbable.

"The first thing I want to do is to examine the brain or, more to the point, our mind, from a different angle. At one time in history, our thoughts were not rational. That is our thoughts were, as many of our thoughts still are, merely subjective events and not apprehensions of objective truth. They responded to external stimuli.

"Now natural selection operates by eliminating responses that are biologically hurtful and by multiplying those which increase the chance of survival. But it is not conceivable that any improvement of responses could ever turn them into acts of insight. The relation between response and stimulus is quite different from that between knowledge and the truth known."

"I didn't quite get that," another member said.

"Well, for example," Lewis responded, "our physical vision is a far more useful response to light than that of a cruder organism which only has a few light-sensitive cells. But neither this improvement nor any possible improvement could bring it an inch nearer to being a knowledge of light! There is something in our mind without which we would not have that knowledge.

"Mere responses and not even experience could amount to the mental behavior which we call reason. It could not have developed from a mental behavior which was originally not rational. There must have been a supernatural influence. In this sense, something beyond nature operates whenever we reason, especially when we use reason for moral judgments. Otherwise we would have to admit that good and evil are only illusions. Thus the rational and moral element in each human mind is a point of force from the supernatural, that is God, working its way into nature.

"Now let's look into the question whether miracles are possible. We cannot rely on experience to answer this question because experience, even if prolonged for a million years, cannot tell us if a thing is possible. By experiment we can tell what regularly happens in nature; we can determine the norm, the rule. A miracle is, by definition, an exception to this rule. Can the discovery of a rule tell you whether, with sufficient cause, the rule can be suspended? It can not! And I suggest that experience cannot tell us that the rule has never been suspended.

"I think it is inaccurate to define a miracle as something which breaks the laws of nature. It doesn't. If I knock out my pipe—that is, if I were allowed to smoke right now—I alter the position of a great many atoms. Nature digests this event with perfect ease. I have simply thrown one event into the general cataract of events. If God annihilates a unit of matter he simply creates a new situation. Nature immediately adapts to this new situation, it finds itself conforming to all the laws. If God creates a miraculous spermatozoon in the body of a virgin, the spermatozoon does not proceed to break any laws; the laws at once take it over. Nature is ready; pregnancy follows, according to all the normal laws, and nine months later a child is born.

"But why would God create miracles? Why would he correct his own work in this way? Well, the reason we have to answer that question is because we think about it the wrong way. Let's suppose a race of people whose peculiar mental limitations compels them to regard a painting as something made up of little colored dots which have been put together like a mosaic. Studying this painting with a magnifying glass they discover more and more complicated relationships between the dots and, with great toil, sort these relationships into regularities. But if they conclude that any departure from these regularities would be unworthy of the painter, they will be far astray. And so, if we conclude that a miracle would be unworthy of the Creator, we would be far astray, because we have no grasp of the creation as a whole.

"Now, what is the probability of a miracle occurring? That depends, really, on how uniform nature is. If nature were perfectly uniform a miracle would not only not be probable, it would be impossible. But nature is not uniform. We believe that nature is uniform, that there is never any deviation from the rules, because we want to believe this. A universe which is unpredictable is inconvenient to us, it is detestable, it shocks us. Thus we have a strong bias to believe that nothing outside the rules ever happens. But that isn't so. Nature, in fact, is a mass of irregularities. The stove which lit yesterday doesn't light today. The water, which was plentiful last year, is scarce this year.

"The question, 'Do miracles occur?' and the question, 'Is the course of Nature absolutely uniform?' are in fact the same questions asked in different ways. And so we come to the conclusion that it is not only possible but also probable that miracles did and do happen."

"Thank you, Mr. Lewis," the chairman said.

"Mr. Lewis," a committee member at the table, who had been nervously tapping his finger, said, "are you by any chance familiar with Philostratus?"

"I can't say that I am," Lewis replied.

"Philostratus was a Roman writer," the member said, "about 200 AD. He tells us the story of Appolonius of Tyana. A young woman, who was about to be married, had died. Her father was a Consul and because of that all Rome mourned. In the presence of a large crowd Appolonius touched the young woman and she came back to life. Would you say this story is true?"

"Probably not," Lewis answered.

"How about this one: in Greece, in the temple of Asklepios, a number of miracles are reported to have happened. For example a story is told about Cleo, a woman who was five years pregnant. She spent a night in this temple. After she left in the morning she gave birth to a son who immediately washed himself in the spring and then walked home with his mother. You don't think this is true either, do you?"

"No," replied Lewis.

"I take it you reject these miracles because they are Roman and Greek and not Christian. Do you mean to say that miracles are possible only within the Christian faith?"

"No, I don't mean to say that," Lewis replied, "it is possible that God created a miracle with the Romans or the Greeks, but it really doesn't make much sense that he should. Christian miracles have a much greater intrinsic probability in virtue of their organic connection with each other and with the whole structure of the Christian religion."

"And that's your considered opinion?" the member said.

"It is," Lewis replied.

"You know, Mr. Lewis," the member continued, "your proof that miracles can happen is a very curious one. Your approach is to first prove, in your own peculiar way that God exists. And then you say: because God exists, miracles are possible. Full circle, Mr. Lewis, you proved precisely nothing!"

"I don't agree with you," Lewis said.

"Any other questions?" the chairman asked.

The members shook their heads.

"Okay, who wants to go next?"

Another member raised his hand. "I would like to bring in David Hume. He wrote a treatise on miracles in 1748 which has still a lot of force today."

"Any objections?"

None of the members objected.

David Hume was brought in. He recognized me and shook my hand. "I see you are still pursuing the subject, Mr. Penter."

C. S. Lewis got out of the chair and David Hume took his place.

"Mr. Hume," the member who had requested him said, "you published an essay entitled *On Miracles* in your *Enquiry Concerning Human Understanding*. Would you tell us what you wrote in this essay?"

"The entire essay?" asked Hume.

"Perhaps a summary?"

Hume collected his thoughts for a moment and then started. "First two observations. The maxim by which we commonly conduct ourselves in our reasoning is, that the objects of which we have no experience resemble those of which we have. But, although we readily reject any report which is unusual and incredible in an ordinary degree, in the case of the utterly absurd and miraculous we seem to disregard this maxim. The passion of surprise and wonder, being an agreeable emotion, gives a tendency toward the belief of such events. And there is a great deal of pride and delight in telling miraculous stories and exciting the admiration of others.

"In my time the miraculous account of travellers, their description of sea and land monsters, their relations of wonderful adventures were received with greediness and the pleasure of telling a piece of news so exciting, of being the first reporter of it, spread the account rapidly. But if the spirit of religion joins itself to the love of wonder, there is an end to common sense. Human testimony, in these circumstances, loses all pretensions of authority.

"The second observation is this: Supernatural and miraculous events are observed chiefly among ignorant nations. If a civilized people has accounts of them, it is found that they were received from ignorant ancestors, who transmitted them with that inviolable sanction and authority which always attend received opinions. When we peruse the first histories of all nations, we are apt to imagine ourselves transported in some new world, where the whole frame of nature is disjointed, and every element performs its operation in a different manner from what it does at present. Battles, revolutions, pestilence, famine and death are never the effect of natural causes. Prodigies, omens and oracles quite obscure the few natural events that are intermingled with them. But as the miracles grow thinner every page, in proportion as we advance nearer the enlightened ages, we soon learn that there is nothing mysterious or supernatural.

"Now then, we hesitate accepting evidence which is contradicted by other evidence. If a hundred people tell me one thing and fifty another, I am doubtful; I would have to take into consideration the character of the witnesses, the manner of the delivery of the testimony, the circumstances, and whether the witnesses have any interest in what they say. In this manner I would weigh the testimony of either side and believe the one which outweighs the other; but I would still proportion my belief to the evidence.

"If now a person or a few persons appear—or are reported to have appeared—and an event is claimed to have been observed, and this report contradicts the observations of thousands of other people, I would then require evidence so strong that it outweighs the evidence of all those other people. Such evidence, to my knowledge, has never been offered for any miracle."

"Thank you, Mr. Hume," the member said. "I would like to point out that Mr. Hume wrote his essay more than 200 years ago. How little progress we sometimes make!"

"Mr. Hume," another member said, "you haven't actually disproven any miracles, have you?"

"No, I have not."

The chairman looked around the table. "Any other questions?" After none of the members spoke up he said: "Thank you, Mr. Hume, and you too, Mr. Lewis."

Both left the room. The chairman continued: "It seems to me we are getting close to the crux of the matter. If we want to say: no miracle has ever happened, do we need to disprove every single miracle?"

Several committee members started talking at once. The chairman pointed at one. "That would make the task quite impossible," the member said. "There are millions of claimed miracles and many date from such a long time ago that reliable evidence is no longer available. If miracles are indeed only illusions of superstitious people, could we not determine that from a representative sample of cases?''

"Ladies and gentlemen," the chairman said, "I agree with that and I have taken the liberty of hiring an investigator who is ready to report to us today. With your concurrence I shall now call him."

The member nodded and murmured concurrence.

The investigator was brought in, a broadshouldered man with a cigar in his mouth.

"What have you been able to find out?" the chairman asked him.

The investigator looked around the table. Realizing that he was the only one smoking in the room he took a last puff on the cigar and elaborately put it out.

"I have found two men who investigated miracles and came to some interesting conclusions. I would like to bring them in later but may I first point out something else?"

"Please do," the chairman said.

"It appears that we have learned a lot in recent years about the human memory. If I'm not mistaken this has a direct bearing on the credibility of reports of miracles."

"You mean that our memory is unreliable?" the chairman asked.

"I have known that for some time, I keep forgetting my wife's birthday," one of the members added and elicited sympathetic laughter.

"No, I don't mean that," the investigator said sternly. "What I mean is that the human memory can be altered without a person being aware of it. This knowledge has come to light by staging traffic accidents and taking down the accounts of a group of witnesses under controlled conditions. If, for example, I ask the witnesses the question: Did the blue car stop at the intersection?, the majority of witnesses will remember a blue car, even if none of the cars involved was blue. In other words, by asking subtle leading questions I can change the witnesses' memory.''

"You don't mean 'change the memory','' the chairman said, "you mean the witness will accommodate the questioner.''

"No,'' the investigator said patiently, "I mean exactly 'change the memory.' The witness does not lie, does not realize that his memory is wrong. The original information is totally lost and replaced by the false information. Even under hypnosis only the false information will come out.''

"And you say this can be caused simply by asking a leading question?'' the chairman asked.

"Yes,'' the investigator nodded. "The effect becomes stronger if peer pressure is involved. If a witness is asked to identify a suspect he or she is quite likely to conform to the majority opinion and then really believe his or her own identification to the point where he or she will swear to it. There are many examples of convictions based on grossly wrong identifications.''

"If I get your point,'' said the chairman, "you are implying that a witness to a miracle may actually and honestly remember a miracle even if no miracle took place.''

"Yes, especially if the witness is easily influenced and has been taught that miracles do happen. And the memory of a miracle can spread to a whole group through peer pressure.''

"All right,'' the chairman said, "we will take that under advisement. Would you like to present the men you mentioned now?''

The investigator went out of the room and came back with an elderly gentleman.

"This is Andrew Dickson White, born in 1832 in New York State. After studying at Yale and in Europe he became a professor of history and English literature at the

University of Michigan. In 1865 he was a co-founder of Cornell University and became its first president. He served as minister to Germany and Russia and later as ambassador to Germany and president of the U.S. delegation at the Hague peace conference. He wrote a number of books. One is entitled *The History of the Warfare of Science with Theology in Christendom,* published in 1896.

"Mr. White, in volume one of this book you have a fascinating story about St. Francis Xavier and his miracles which I am sure this committee would like to hear."

"Francis Xavier," White began, "was born in 1506 in Navarre, now part of Spain. He studied in Paris where he met Ignatius Loyola and became part of the founding group of the Society of Jesus, better known as the Jesuits. he was a missionary, very selfless, who travelled to India, the Malay Archipelago and to the newly discovered Japan. He died on his way to China in 1552.

"Now the reason I singled out Francis Xavier in my book is that we have an excellent and extremely detailed record of his activities by himself and his closest associates in their original form and all documents I have relied on for this story have been published under the sanction of the Catholic church.

"None of Francis Xavier's letters or those of his associates mentions that he had performed any miracles during his life. In fact Joseph Acosta, a provincial in the Jesuit order, laments in 1571 that 'the reason why progress in the world's conversion to Christianity is not as rapid as in the early apostolic times lies in the missionaries themselves, because there is now no power of working miracles.' And, in fact, he refers to Francis Xavier by name.

"A few years after Xavier's death the first stories of miracles appear, miracles which Francis Xavier was supposed to have performed during his life. In 1594, 42 years after his death, the first biography is published, written by a Father Tursellinus. In it we find a sizeable number of miracles. In 1622 the canonization proceedings begin in Rome to declare Francis Xavier a saint. During these proceedings ten miracles are discussed and accepted. In the Catholic church at least four proven miracles must have been performed by a person to be named a saint.

"Also in 1622, that is 70 years after his death, a biography written by a Father Vitelleschi is published and here we find an even larger number of miracles. And, finally, in 1682, 130 years after Francis Xavier's death, a biography by Father Bouhours was published which became a standard reference work. In it we find a much larger number of miracles still.

"Now it must be remembered that for any of these biographies no new evidence had become available. All the first-hand witnesses were dead and all the first-hand documents had been available at the time of Francis Xavier's death. Yet in Tursellinus, Xavier during his life raises four persons from the dead, in Bouhours fourteen. In Tursellinus Xavier is transfigured twice, in Bouhours five times!

"It is interesting to follow particular events. For example, Tursellinus writes that, on the voyage from Goa to Malacca, Xavier, having left the ship and gone to an island, was afterwards found by the persons sent in search of him so deeply absorbed in prayer as to be unmindful of all things around him. Eighty-eight years later Bouhours writes: 'The servants found the man of God raised from the ground into the air, his eyes fixed upon heaven, and rays of light about his countenance'.

"And then there is the story of the crucifix. Xavier tells in his correspondence that his crucifix fell overboard and that he was sad because of the loss. Tursellinus writes that the crucifix fell overboard, but that it was later brought to shore by a crab. In Bouhour we read that the saint threw the crucifix into the sea to still a tempest and that a crab handed it to him on the shore.

"There are numerous such enlargements; I only want to mention one more. Xavier tells us of the great difficulties he had with the various languages of the different tribes and nations. He tells us that sometimes he managed to learn just enough of a language to translate some of the main church formulas. Sometimes he employed interpreters and sometimes he even used sign language. His trip to China was delayed because the interpreter he hired failed to meet him.

"On this subject Tursellinus does not enlarge. In fact he tells us: 'Nothing was a greater impediment to him than his ignorance of the Japanese tongues. Repeatedly, when some uncouth expression offended their fastidious and delicate ears, the awkward speech of Francis was the cause of laughter'.

"Bouhours tells us that 'the holy man spoke very well the language of those Barbarians without having learned it and had no need of an interpreter'. And at another place: 'He preached in the afternoon to the Japanese in their language, but so naturally and with so much ease that he could not be taken for a foreigner'.

"In 1622, at the canonization proceedings, it was declared that Francis Xavier had the miraculous gift of tongues, that he spoke to the various tribes with ease in their own language. The miracles of the gift of tongues and the crab with the crucifix were specifically included in the papal bull issued by Urban VIII declaring Francis Xavier a saint."

The chairman looked in surprise and said, "A papal bull, that is an infallible statement by the pope, is it not?"

"It is," White said.

"There is some controversy about this," a member objected, "the first Vatican council redefined papal infallibility in 1870."

"Well, let's not get sidetracked by this," the chairman said. "But here seems to be a case where a miracle was proclaimed by the hierarchy of the Catholic Church, despite clear evidence to the contrary."

"But it's just one example, isn't it," a member who had not spoken before said.

"I have a second witness," the investigator offered.

"Let's hear him," the chairman said and thanked White.

The investigator took White out of the room and came back with another man. "This is Dr. William Nolen." Dr. Nolen sat down at the foot of the table.

"Dr. Nolen, would you tell us a little bit about yourself?"

"Certainly," Dr. Nolen replied. "I was born in Holyoke, Massachusetts and graduated from Holy Cross and Tufts Medical School. I spent five years at Bellevue and two years in the Army Medical Corps. I am a fellow of the American College of Surgeons and my practice as a surgeon is in Litchfield, Minnesota."

"Dr. Nolen," the investigator asked, "in 1972 you started an investigation into miracle or faith healing which lasted two years and on which you reported in a book. What started you on this investigation?"

"Well," Dr. Nolen answered, "one of my patients was allegedly cured by a Filipino psychic surgeon. That is, this miracle healer performed surgery without the use of a knife and without leaving any scars."

"You travelled to the Philippines to investigate this, did you not?"

"I did," Dr. Nolen answered.

"And what did you find?"

"The whole thing was a fake. The miracle surgeon had cotton and a red liquid hidden in the palm of his hand. He started kneading the patient's stomach and then pulled out the organs that he removed which were actually just pieces of cotton soaked in the red liquid. After the operation he wiped off the 'blood' and no scar could be seen."

"You also investigated a fellow named Norbu Chen."

"Yes, in Texas," Dr. Nolen said, "I was told by Edgar Mitchell, the former astronaut, that Norbu Chen had demonstrated miraculous healing power. I went to see Chen in Houston and observed his healing technique. He claims to have spent three years in Sikkim in the Himalayas and there to have been taught by a lama to float in the air, to move into someone else's body, to make things appear and disappear and, of course, to heal people."

"How did he do that?"

"He said a few magic words over the patient for a few minutes."

"How many patients did he have?"

"Enough to give him an income of about half a million dollars per year."

"Did he in fact heal people?"

"No," Dr. Nolen answered, "none of the ones I checked up on were healed."

"But I don't understand this," the chairman said, "you are saying that people are willing to travel all the way to the Philippines or to pay Norbu Chen a large amount of money, yet no one has ever been healed?"

"Well," Dr. Nolen said, "the whole subject of miracle healing needs an explanation. You see, the human body has a tremendous capacity to heal itself. For example, if someone has a broken bone and is young enough, the bone will heal even if the broken parts are badly aligned. There are cases where the broken pieces met at an angle of as much as 30 degrees, yet the bone healed and straightened itself out perfectly.

"Even a physician does not really heal. The best we can do is to make it easier for the body to heal itself. So, when a patient is cured, a doctor can't really claim that he healed the patient.

"Now, in the human body there are two nervous systems, a voluntary one and an autonomous one. When I pick up a glass of water I use my voluntary nervous system. I make a decision and my brain tells the muscles what to do.

"The autonomous nervous system controls the heart, the lungs, eyes, blood vessels, intestines, bladder, etc. For example, if you shine a light into someone's eye in a dark room, the pupil will contract. Now that person did not make a decision to contract the pupil, it happened automatically, controlled by the autonomous nervous system.

"Let's consider a patient with an ulcer in the duodenum—that's the first part of the small intestines. This is the area where 90% of all stomach ulcers occur.

"The cells of the stomach wall produce hydrochloric acid, used to digest food. When we eat, a nerve, called the vagus nerve, stimulates the acid-producing cells. The vagus nerve is part of the autonomous nervous system. Now suppose that the vagus nerve begins to malfunction; it stimulates the acid-producing cells too often and too long and the quantity of acid is consistently too large. After a while that acid burns a hole into the wall of the duodenum. If the acid overproduction continues the hole will go all the way through the wall and erode blood vessels and hemorrhaging starts, a bleeding ulcer.

"How do I cure this? I can prescribe antacids to neutralize the acid. I can give the patient pills which work on the stomach cells and reduce acid production; or I can remove the defective part of the stomach by surgery.

"But the real cause of the problem is the vagus nerve, over which I have no direct control. I can't simply tell it to stop stimulating as I tell my hand to lift. But we know from experience that tension and anxiety cause the vagus nerve to overreact. And it is quite often possible to 'cure' an ulcer through hypnosis or by simply making the patient aware as to what caused the ulcer in the first place.

"What I am driving at here is the power of suggestion. Although we do not have direct control over the autonomous nervous system, it can be influenced indirectly. If a faith healer lays on his hands and says: 'I rebuke that ulcer', and if the patient believes, the activity of the vagus nerve will slow down. The same is true for Norbu Chen or a Filippino psychic surgeon. If the patient is convinced that the healer has removed the defective organ, an improvement will occur, if the illness is due to a malfunction of the autonomous nervous system.

"Faith healers can also be successful with neurotic and hysterical illnesses. Let me give you an example. A woman patient of mine, whose husband had died in a car accident, caught a cold, developed laryngitis and from that point on could only talk in a whisper. There was nothing wrong with her vocal cords; what happened was that she blamed herself for her husband's death. She was punishing herself for arguing with her husband the night of his fatal accident.

"Four years later she had problems with her gall bladder and needed an operation. After the operation I told her that, in giving her the anesthetic, I had to insert a tube into her windpipe and I noticed that part of her vocal cords were stuck together and I was able to spread them apart. I had made the whole thing up, but the next morning she was able to talk normally again. Anyone with enough power of suggestion could have achieved the same result.

"But if the organ itself is diseased this kind of 'healing' is not possible. No miracle healer can remove cancer, for example."

"Tell us about Kathryn Kuhlman," the investigator said.

95

"Kathryn Kuhlman is a well-known faith healer and has written several books," Dr. Nolen said. "While I was preparing to go to the Philippines she had a service scheduled in Minneapolis. I had heard that Kathryn Kuhlman's services regularly filled huge auditoriums and hundreds or even thousands of people were cured during each service. She claims that she heals through the Holy Spirit. So I signed on as an usher in the wheelchair section and as a doctor in attendance. I had two legal secretaries take down the names and addresses of those healed so that I could follow them up later. I also interviewed Kathryn Kuhlman.

"It was a very unusual experience. A lot of people walked up the stage and afterward claimed to have been cured. People with diabetes, heart conditions, bursitis and even cancer. Our two secretaries were able to take down 82 names of people who felt they had been cured during the service. There were hundreds of others they could not talk to because of the tumult and excitement."

"Did you find any cures?"

"No," Dr. Nolen said, "none. There was one girl, for example, 18 years old, who had multiple sclerosis. She had trouble walking. She said she had felt a tingling sensation in her back when Kathryn Kuhlman said: 'Go into the aisle, you people with spine injury, but don't come up to the stage until you know that you have been healed.' After this she walked onto the stage and felt she had been healed. But our later investigation showed that there had been no change at all.

"A young man of 21 with cancer of the liver felt that he had been cured. He died 12 days later.

"A fifty-year-old woman with cancer of the stomach, liver and vertebrae thought she was cured and walked onto the stage without her backbrace. The next morning she woke up with a horrible back-pain. One of the cancerous vertebrae had collapsed; she died of cancer four months later.

"There was a sort of mass hysteria at this service. I had been suffering from bursitis of the elbow for some time. Whenever Kathryn Kuhlman said 'There is somebody being cured of bursitis right now' I found myself moving my elbow back and forth to see if the pain was gone. A couple of times, for a few seconds, I actually thought I was cured."

"Are you saying, then, Dr. Nolen," the chairman asked, "that as far as you were able to determine no miracle healing took place but many people—including yourself for a few seconds—believed that miracles had happened?"

"Exactly," Dr. Nolen answered.

"Do you believe in God, Dr. Nolen?"

"Yes, I do."

"Could I ask what religion you belong to?" the chairman asked.

"I am a Catholic," Dr. Nolen answered.

"Thank you, Dr. Nolen," the chairman said.

5
Jesus Christ

The fire crackled as I threw a new log on it. It was past midnight but I was not tired. I went back to my chair, picked up the book and, absorbed in thought studied the spine: *The Quest of the Historical Jesus,* by Albert Schweitzer.

The heroic figure of Albert Schweitzer was very much on my mind. He was born in 1875 in Alsace, now part of France, then part of Germany. His father was a Lutheran pastor. Schweitzer studied theology and philosophy, receiving doctorates in both fields. In addition he earned a doctorate in music and became one of the world's foremost organists and interpreters of Bach.

At age 25, at the turn of the century, he began a study of the historical accuracy of the life of Jesus. A number of books had appeared during the latter half of the 19th century which were critical toward the Christian teachings about Jesus. Schweitzer set out to answer these critics. But he slowly began to realize that all was not well and that there was some substance in this criticism.

He published his findings in 1906. It was a brutally honest book and, coming from a brilliant theologian, it had an immediate, reverberating influence.

Shortly after the publication of the *Quest of the*

Historical Jesus he abruptly abandoned his career as a preacher and lecturer and studied medicine, earning his fourth doctorate in 1913. He then went to Lambarene in the African jungle, set up a hospital and spent the rest of his life on this project, occasionally giving organ concerts throughout Europe to raise money and writing on philosophy, theology and peace. For the last thirty years of his life he was one of the most admired men in the world.

I suddenly was stirred out of my thoughts by a movement in the chair next to mine. I stared at the tall man with the large mustache and the full head of unkempt, white hair: Albert Schweitzer.

I looked at him for some time. I had seen his picture many times. Yet in person he looked different. There was something tragic in his face.

"Dr. Schweitzer," I finally said, sitting up straight in my chair, "I don't quite understand your feelings about Jesus. You don't seem to agree with any of these critics, but you come to the same conclusions."

"It is somewhat difficult to explain," Schweitzer answered. "We know so little about Jesus, almost nothing. In trying to reconstruct the life of Jesus their own way each of these critics included his own prejudices. So I didn't agree with any particular critic in detail, but I had to agree with their general conclusion that much of what we believe about Jesus is mere fiction."

"Why? Don't we have four independent accounts?"

"No. In the gospel of John, Jesus is a freely imagined person. This gospel is almost entirely legend. Luke is very doubtful wherever it goes beyond Mark and Matthew. And in Matthew the first two chapters are almost certainly fiction."

"That leaves Paul, Mark and parts of Matthew. Don't they give us a complete account of Jesus?"

"Paul tells us almost nothing about the historical Jesus. Mark and Matthew are misleading if they are read without knowing the beliefs within Judaism at the time of Jesus. You see, at that time many Jewish sects believed that the world would shortly come to an end and that, with the coming of the Messiah a new Kingdom of God would be formed. Jesus himself believed that. Without taking this into consideration, Jesus is a stranger to our time.''

Schweitzer stared into the fire. ''But you are asking the wrong question. What is important about Jesus is the amount of influence over mankind his doctrine of love has won. It is the spiritual and ethical truth of Christianity that has remained the same throughout the centuries, not dogma. It doesn't matter whether his religion came into existence within a Jewish expectation of the end of the world or any other framework.''

''That is not exactly the accepted Christian view.'' The voice had come from the dark part of the room. I turned on the light. Two men were sitting there.

The one who had spoken, a clergyman, pointed at Schweitzer and said: ''Ask him if he considers himself a Christian.''

''Do you consider yourself a Christian?'' I asked Schweitzer.

''I do,'' Schweitzer answered.

''He might be a much better Christian than you, Reverend,'' the other man said.

''Quite wrong,'' the Reverend said. ''Critics like you or Dr. Schweitzer simply aren't important. They come and go, they proclaim their own fancy theories which become a fad for a while and then disappear. Christianity has survived your kind for almost 2000 years.''

''What about the claim that the gospels are unreliable, Reverend?'' I asked.

''That is simply a matter of wrong emphasis. Instead of focusing on unimportant inconsistencies between the gospels, we should bear in mind the important things: that we have not one but four parallel accounts and that much in these accounts is corroborated by a number of contemporary writers . . . ''

"Fiddlesticks," the Critic said, "the whole contemporary literature about Jesus amounts to precisely nothing."

"Gentlemen," I broke in, "polemics won't get us anywhere. Could you make an attempt to give me the facts without emotion?"

They both nodded.

"I am interested in hearing your views," I said to the Critic. "I hope you don't mind, Reverend, but I have been exposed to the Christian view much more than to that of its critics."

The Reverend nodded and the Critic stood up and, with his hands behind his back, started to pace as he spoke.

"The life of Jesus is somewhat like a newspaper photograph. If you look at it from a distance you see an image. If you examine it more closely you notice that it consists of dark and light dots. If you look at it through a magnifying glass, the picture makes no sense at all. Thousands of books have been written, examining and interpreting the details of the New Testament which make no sense at all.

"What are our sources on Jesus? He himself wrote nothing. There are no writings about him that were made during his lifetime. The earliest documents relating to Jesus are the letters of Paul; they were written between 49 and 60 AD, or 19 to 30 years after Jesus' death. By his own saying Paul did not know Jesus personally, he became a convert after Jesus had died. And Paul actually tells us almost nothing about Jesus.

"Then we have the four gospels. The earliest one is Mark. It was written sometime between 64 and 70 AD, that is a little more than a generation after Jesus. Mark is the shortest of the four gospels; it was written in Greek for Greek-speaking gentiles.

"For a long time it was believed that Mark was one of the apostles, but there is now almost universal agreement among Bible scholars that this is not true. He may have been a follower of the apostle Peter, but even this is not certain. Whoever the author was, he had no first-hand knowledge of Jesus.

"In the gospel of Mark Jesus never refers to himself as God or as the 'Son of God'; he speaks of himself only as the 'Son of Man'. In Mark Jesus dies a lonely death, foresaken by everybody, even his closest disciples.

"The most controversial part of Mark is the conclusion, chapter 16, verses 9 through 20, where Jesus rises from the dead, appears to his followers and ascends into heaven. In some of the early copies this part is absent, in some there is a different ending. It is more than likely that this part was added later.

"Next comes Matthew. Written sometime between 70 and 80 AD, it depicts Jesus as a royal messiah, the last king of Israel, a descendent from David. For the first time he is called 'Son of God'. There is a great emphasis in this gospel on fulfillment of Old Testament prophecies and Matthew also has details of Jesus' infancy which are not recorded anywhere else. As Dr. Schweitzer said, this part of Matthew was almost certainly added later.

"We don't know who the author of Matthew was either. As with Mark, Matthew's name was given to this gospel under the false early assumption that he was an apostle. Like Mark, he did not know Jesus. The author of Matthew copied Mark, using almost the entire contents of Mark, and he also copied another book or roll, from which Luke also copied, a book now lost.

"The third gospel is Luke, written around the year 80 AD, or two generations after the death of Jesus. He uses 60% of Mark and this material fills about a third of Luke;

another 20% of Luke came from the lost book, the source also used by Matthew.

"By his own saying Luke was not an eyewitness. We are not sure who Luke was. He might have been a companion of Paul, but this is a controversial assumption since the writings of Paul and Luke differ on some fundamental issues.

"These three gospels are called the synoptics because they agree with each other much more closely than with the fourth, the gospel of John. This gospel was written later, sometime between 100 and 110 AD, or three generations after the death of Jesus. It broadly contradicts the other three gospels. The author claims to have been Jesus' favorite apostle and the last surviving eyewitness. There is strong evidence and overwhelming agreement among Bible scholars that this claim is not true. John is a complete unknown to us, a man or perhaps a group of people who lived three generations later and used the name of the apostle to lend authority to the document.

"The gospel of John was written without reference to Mark, Matthew and Luke and probably without knowledge of them. While the authors of Mark, Matthew and Luke clearly expect the imminent end of the world and the second coming of Jesus, in John the Kingdom of God has already arrived in the person of Jesus and a complex new theology is presented.

"It must also be mentioned that these four gospels were not the only ones. From the second century on there was a bewildering number of writings about Jesus, many of which claimed to have been written by one of the apostles. There were gospels by Peter, Andrew, Phillip, Thomas, Valentinus, Marcion, Bartholomew, Jude, Barnabas, James, Thaddeus, Merinthus, Tatian and Eve. There was the book of James, the acts of Paul, John and Peter, the revelations of Thomas, the epistle of Polycarp and so on, more than a hundred of them.

"Almost all of these documents were used by the early Christian congregations in their church services. Between the second and the fourth century most of the writings then in use were declared apocryphal . . . "

The Critic stood now in front of the Reverend's chair and bent down, speaking directly to him.

" . . . but we don't know by whom or how this selection was made, do we, Reverend?"

The Reverend stood up, face to face with the Critic. "They were guided by the Holy Spirit, but you wouldn't understand that."

The Critic remained in his position for a second, shrugged his shoulders and then turned around abruptly.

"Now, then, let's consider some individual points of fact. We are examining the life of a person who lived some 2000 years ago. We have no writing by him. The only writings about him originated outside Palestine between one and three generations after his death. None of the writers had known him personally."

"What kind of a man was Jesus? He was a preacher, a wandering rabbi, who was well read in the Old Testament. We have no idea what he looked like. He came from an ordinary family, he was not a descendant of David as most people believe . . . "

"Now you are going too far," the Reverend interrupted. "His lineage to David is well documented."

"Not so, Reverend. There is no such claim in the earliest gospel, Mark. It first appears in Matthew and Luke because by that time the conception of Jesus had changed. Both Matthew and Luke list a genealogy of Jesus. According to Matthew, Jesus was the son of Joseph, who was the son of Jacob . . . and so on through 28 generations to David. Luke does the same thing, only now Joseph was the son of Heli, not Jacob—in fact there is not a single name in Luke's list of ancestors that agrees with Matthew. Luke lists 43 generations from Jesus to David,

Matthew says there were only 28. This whole genealogy, Mr. Penter, is a later invention to make the predictions of the Old Testament come true."

The Critic paused and turned toward the Reverend. The Reverend gestured as though he wanted to say something but then sat down.

"And the same is true," the Critic continued, "for the story about his birth in Bethlehem, in a manger, adored by shepherds, with harkening angels, a mysterious star and foreign wise men. Again, Bethlehem is mentioned only in Matthew and Luke. Bethlehem was David's hometown and in the Old Testament Micah predicted that the ruler of Israel would again come from Bethlehem. But the two writers have again conflicting accounts. Matthew says that Bethlehem was Joseph and Mary's place of residence and that they later moved to Nazareth. According to Luke the parents lived in Nazareth and they had to go to Bethlehem because of a census. But no census took place until 10 years later.

"Matthew also tells us that the family had to flee to Egypt after Jesus' birth because Herod was killing all the children under two years of age in and around the city of Bethlehem. If this is true why did contemporary historians, who recorded the administration of Herod in great detail, not report such a ghastly massacre? The only possible answer here is that these stories are inventions to make some Old Testament predictions come true."

The Critic had again spoken the last sentence directly to the Reverend.

"That seems to be a minor point," the Reverend said.

"Alright. Let's take the story of the virgin birth," the Critic continued. "Mark says nothing about virgin birth and neither does John, in an otherwise very detailed gospel. This idea appears only in Matthew and Luke and their stories conflict once more. For example, Matthew says that the angel announcing the immaculate conception appeared to Joseph. Luke says he appeared to Mary. The idea of virgin birth was very familiar to the Greek speaking people for whom these two gospels were written. Birth by a virgin or conception by a god was told about a great many of the Greek heroes. The legend about Heracles, for example, says that he was born of the virgin Alcmena and that she and her husband Amphitryon travelled from Mycenea to Thebes before Heracles' birth so that the child would have a birthplace different from his home.''

Now the Critic, standing behind the Reverend's chair, put his hands on the backrest and leaned over him. ''Have you ever wondered, Reverend, how the stories of the virgin birth and descendancy from David fit together? If Joseph had nothing to do with the conception of Jesus, why would his ancestry be important?''

''The lineage to David was probably through Mary,'' the Reverend said.

''But that is not what Luke and Matthew claim. And, remember, their accounts were selected with the help of the Holy Ghost.''

''Is the sarcasm really necessary?'' I asked.

''I apologize,'' the Critic said and started pacing again.

''Another point: Jesus never called himself God, Lord, Son of God, Messiah, or Son of David. He called himself only the 'Son of Man', a description of the mythical figure of the judge who will come again on the clouds after the destruction of the world. This description appears in the later apocalyptic writings of the Old Testament which originated in the second century BC, a short while before Jesus.

''His teachings were really not nearly as original as we believe. Some of them are from the Old Testament and some from the sect of the Essenes.''

''I beg your pardon?''

"Essenes," the Critic replied. "You probably heard of the Dead Sea Scrolls."

I nodded.

"With the recent discovery of the Dead Sea Scrolls we now know a great deal of the sect of the Essenes. It had been fairly certain that John the Baptist was at one time a member of the Essene community of Qumran, a monastery founded in the second century BC and destroyed in the first century AD. It was located in the vicinity where the Baptist preached in the desert. Much of the Baptists preachings and some of Jesus' were influenced by the Essenes, who praised poverty, chastity and love of one's enemies; they were strongly against divorce. The Essene writings also mention the 'new covenant' and most importantly, expect the world to end soon.

"Another point: Jesus, during his lifetime, was not an important man. Contemporary non-Christian histories either did not know of him or did not consider him important enough to be mentioned, even though they recorded the happenings in Palestine around that time in great detail."

"Now you really surprise me," the Reverend said, jumping up from his chair. "There is a well-known account of Jesus in Josephus, a contemporary writer who was certainly not a Christian."

"I take it you are referring to Josephus Flavius," the Critic said, smiling at the Reverend, "specifically his book *Of the Antiquities of the Jews.* Would you like to tell us what Josephus said about Jesus?"

"Well, I don't remember it word for word, I would have to get the book . . . "

The Critic, who had held his arms behind his back, suddenly produced a book. "I believe I have it right here, Reverend."

Somewhat bewildered the Reverend accepted the book, searched for the passage and read: 'At that time there

108

lived Jesus, a wise man, if indeed one may call him a man. For he was the doer of marvellous works, a teacher of those who willingly accept the truth and many of the Jews and Greeks became his followers. This was the Christ who was condemned to the cross by Pilate after our own leaders had accused him; but those who loved him did not cease to do so. For he appeared on the third day to them living again as the divine prophets had written about this and many other marvels about him. And from that time forward the Christians, named after him, have never ceased'. That seems to be a very clear statement about Jesus, and written by a non-Christian.''

"Read the next paragraph," the Critic said.

The Reverend glanced at it. "Why? It has nothing to do with Jesus."

"Please read it anyway," the Critic insisted.

"Also at this time another misfortune befell the Jews . . . ''

"Another misfortune befell the Jews?" the Critic exclaimed. "Josephus writes this immediately after he tells us about Christ? That doesn't seem to make any sense!''

The Critic took the book from the Reverend. "The paragraph just above the paragraph about Jesus discusses a revolt by a few thousand Jews against Pilate and how the Roman soldiers put down the rebellion and killed and injured many of them. In other words the paragraph above and the paragraph just below belong together. And that means the paragraph about Jesus was inserted later by a rather inept Christian who found it embarrassing that none of the important books at that time mentioned Jesus. In fact, this paragraph about Jesus does not appear in some of the early copies of Josephus."

"Well, maybe," the Reverend said, "but it seems presumptuous to conclude from this that Jesus was not an important figure during his lifetime. After all, he did start an enormous movement."

109

"Yes, I am puzzled about your statement too," I said to the Critic. "If your view is correct, how did Christianity come about?"

"All right," the Critic replied, resuming his pacing, "let me tell you the story of early Christianity the way I see it. Let me start with the life of Jesus without the Christian legends."

"It can't be done," Albert Schweitzer said.

"I know," the Critic said, "it can't be done with historical accuracy. My story will contain guesses, inaccuracies, my own bias, I admit it; but my story comes much closer to the truth than what we are still being taught in countless religious books and from the pulpit every Sunday."

"Let's hear it," I said.

"Well," the Critic began, "Jesus was born in the year 7 or 6 BC. It is ironic that the counting of years set to start with the birth of Jesus, turned out to be wrong too."

"Do we really need these digressions?" I asked.

The Critic held up his arm in an apologetic way. "We know nothing about him until about age 35. He probably had four brothers and several sisters. It is also likely that his father, Joseph, died early.

"He was a very religious man, having studied the Old Testament in great detail. At age 35 he meets John the Baptist, a wild-looking ascetic who preaches in the desert. Jesus is inspired by him and he decides to become a preacher himself. Like the Baptist and the Essenes, and in fact most of the Jews at that time, he believes that the end of the world is near and that those who are not prepared for it will suffer. So he preaches universal love, asks his followers to give up all wealth and follow him. He sees himself as the last messenger of God.

"At first, in his own hometown of Nazareth, he is not successful. People know him there. So he moves on to other small towns: Magdala, Dalmanutha, Capernaum,

110

Bethsaida and Chorazin, all close together on the shore of the Sea of Galilee. There he meets with success. He develops a following and gains twelve close associates. His movement gathers momentum.

"Convinced that the end of the world is near, he sends out his disciples by twos into the cities of Israel that they might spread the word. He tells them that, before they have a chance to return, the world will end with terrible suffering."

The Critic moved toward Albert Schweitzer. "But nothing happens. The disciples return. And that is what you discovered, Dr. Schweitzer, that . . . "

"That Jesus was capable of error," Schweitzer said.

"Yes. And, therefore . . . " the Critic continued, trying to prompt Schweitzer. But Schweitzer only stared into the fire.

"And, therefore, Jesus was not God," the Critic said slowly. The fire reflected eerily on Schweitzer's face. He nodded almost imperceptibly.

The Critic looked at me and then continued. "Jesus now doesn't know what to do. He withdraws. He re-reads or remembers chapter 53 of Isaiah which speaks of a man who suffered and died as a sacrifice for the sins of his people. He is now convinced that he is this 'Son of Man', that he must die for his people and that, after his death, he will reappear, as Isaiah had said, on the clouds as the Judge.

"With this new conviction he re-emerges, tells his followers what will happen and goes to Jerusalem. There he deliberately provokes the ruling class, drives the merchants and moneychangers out of the temple, upsets their tables and blocks the traffic of goods into the temple grounds. He is arrested, quickly tried, and convicted of blasphemy, an offense punishable by death. His case is brought before the Roman administrator Pilate and Jesus

111

does not defend himself. So Pilate ratifies the death warrant and Jesus is executed the following morning.

"What happened next? Did Jesus rise from the dead? Did he ascend into heaven? Let us look, again, at the evidence.

"First, was there anything unusual about Jesus' death? Mark and Luke say that a darkness fell over the whole land at noon and lasted for three hours and that the curtain of the temple was torn in half. Matthew adds to this that there was an earthquake, that graves opened and many saints were raised from the dead and entered the holy city where many saw them.

"Why is it that Mark and Luke do not report such a momentous happening as many people rising from the dead and showing themselves in Jerusalem the moment Jesus dies? Why is it that none of the non-Christian reporters of that time noticed anything, neither a darkness in midday, nor the inexplicably torn curtain nor the dead coming out of their graves and entering the city? And why is it that John knows nothing at all about any of these happenings?

"Then the resurrection. Mark says that three women visited the grave on Sunday morning, found the stone rolled away, the body gone and an angel sitting at the right-hand side. Matthew says there were two women, that they experienced a violent earthquake, that then an angel descended from heaven, rolled the stone away and sat on it. In Luke there are three women who find the stone rolled away and suddenly two angels appear on either side of them. In John only Mary of Magdala goes to the grave, sees that the stone has been removed, runs to get Peter and John, who find the body gone and then, later, two angels appear to Mary of Magdala, one sitting at the head and one at the foot of the grave. A very confusing story.

"About the appearance of Jesus after his death there is even more confusion in the gospels. According to Matthew the eleven remaining apostles marched to Galilee the same day to meet Jesus on a mountain as they had been told to do by the angel. Luke and John report that this meeting took place at the same time in Jerusalem behind locked doors.

"On the ascension into heaven Mark says that Jesus was taken up into heaven in Jerusalem immediately after the meeting with the eleven apostles. Luke says that it happened in Bethany and much later. Matthew and John know nothing at all about any ascension.

"What are we to believe about Jesus' death, resurrection and ascension? We have here contradictions in four scrolls written by people who readily believed in the supernatural. Second-hand reports, written between 35 and 80 years later, with the purpose of converting Greek-speaking Jews to Christianity. The authors and their audiences were surrounded and influenced by Greek and Roman mythology. Is it so surprising to find resurrection and ascension in these gospels when the popular religions of that time, against which Christianity was competing, were full of such beliefs? Adonis, for example, was said to have been buried in a rocky grave, was resurrected, and ascended into heaven. Heracles' body, according to Greek mythology, was placed on Mt. Oiti and ascended into heaven. Mithra, the god of the main rival religion during early Christianity, died, was resurrected and ascended into heaven in a chariot.''

The Critic paused for a few seconds to collect his thoughts.

"Jesus had a powerful message, certainly, and he was there at the right time. But what happened after Jesus' death is even more important than what happened during his lifetime.

"Jesus dies on the cross. His followers remember what he said: that he will come again as the 'Son of Man' when the world ends and the 'Kingdom of God' begins and that this will take place soon. Under James, the brother of Jesus, they continue his missionary work and live in poverty in communes.

"Now the second founder of Christianity appears. He is Paul of Tarsus, a Greek-speaking Jew, who is converted after Jesus' death. He does not accept the leadership of the group in Jerusalem under James but develops his own, significantly modified theology. His idea is that Jesus has died for our sins. He brings his message to Syria, Turkey, Greece and Rome and is much more successful than the original group in Jerusalem. He extends his missionary work to pagans and now, only now, does the name Christians appear, followers of the anointed one.

"But up to this point the entire thrust of the new movement is that the world will end soon and that the followers will have to save themselves by giving up everything and following Christ. And that is the reason why there are no earlier written accounts of Jesus' life. Since the world is to end soon, it doesn't make much sense to make a record for posterity.

"But the end of the world still doesn't happen. It becomes difficult to believe the message. And slowly, over two generations, a third theology develops: No longer are the Christians waiting for the imminent return of Jesus; the belief is transformed into a hope of reunion with Him after death. Now the Kingdom of God, which they believed would be on earth, is moved to heaven. That is the time the gospel of John was written.

"Numerous Christian sects develop. By the year 187 there are some 20. By 384 there are 80. To counter this dissipation, a central organization, a church forms, headquartered no longer in Jerusalem, but in Rome, the capital of the empire.

"Within the Roman empire this church thrives because its rivals, the old Greek, Persian and Roman mythologies,

114

are at their end; they have become overgrown with unbelievable myths.

"As the Christians grow in numbers and acquire
wealth and power, they become a political force. In 312
the Roman emperor Constantine declares Christianity the
state religion. It was this political move which gave Christianity the basis from which it grew."

The Critic sat down. The Reverend shook his head. "A
very convenient story. You left out just one factor."

"And what is that?" the Critic asked.

"God."

The Critic, with a resigned grimace, shook his head.

6
Religion

The judge entered the courtroom through the door behind the bench and ceremonially took his seat. He rapped his gavel and the murmuring in the courtroom stopped abruptly.

I looked around me. The courtroom was packed, yet, oddly, the seats next to mine were empty. I suddenly realized that I was sitting in the jury section, alone. It was too late to move.

"Mr. Prosecutor," the judge called out, "are you ready with your next witness?"

"I am, your honor," the Prosecutor answered, "I call to the stand Bertrand Russell."

Bertrand Russell, thin, old and hawkish, stood up and took the witness stand.

The Prosecutor walked a few steps toward him, put his thumbs in his vest and said, "Lord Russell, in many of your books you voiced a very definite opinion about religion. Could you give this court your view?"

"It would give me great pleasure," Russell said. "I am quite convinced that religion has done and is doing more harm than good. Throughout history religion has been the chief source of intolerance, hatred and bloodshed."

"Objection," the Defender shouted and sprung up.

"This is pure supposition, an inflammatory statement without substance."

"I believe Lord Russell is about to substantiate it," the Prosecutor said.

"Let's have a little tolerance here," the judge said to the defender. "I think we are all capable of separating polemics from facts." He turned toward the witness: "Can you substantiate this, Mr. Russell?"

"Yes, I believe I can," Russell answered. "Let's take the concept of righteousness, so often advocated by religious people. What is righteousness? Well, if there is righteousness, there must also be unrighteousness, and that is simply behavior of the kind disliked by the majority. The majority arranges an elaborate system of ethics around what it calls righteousness and then feels justified in wreaking punishment upon the objects of its own dislikes. Through this concept it enhances its own self-esteem and gives respectability to conceit and hatred.

"The attitude of the Church toward sex is such an example, an attitude both morbid and unnatural. In fact the whole concept of sin in Christian ethics does an extraordinary amount of harm.

"We sometimes hear talk that Christianity has improved the status of women. This is one of the grossest perversions of history. Woman in Christianity is considered primarily as the temptress, the inspirer of impure lusts. The teaching has been, and still is, that virginity is best, but that for those who find this impossible marriage is permissible. 'It is better to marry than to burn', as St. Paul brutally puts it.

"But above all this, religion, especially Christianity, has created a totally wrong emphasis on virtue. In the Christian view the virtuous man is one who retires from the world; the only men of action who are regarded as saints are those who wasted the lives of their subjects on fighting infidels. The church would never regard a man as a saint because he reformed the finances, or the criminal law, or the judiciary. Such paltry contributions to human welfare are of no importance.

"In religion it is thought to be virtuous to have faith, to have a conviction which cannot be shaken by contrary evidence. This produces hostility toward evidence and causes us to close our minds to every fact that doesn't suit our prejudices."

"Thank you, Lord Russell," the Prosecutor said.

The Defender got up. "Tell me, Mr. Russell, can't you think of anything positive about religion?"

Russell thought for a moment. "Well, it helped fix the calendar."

There was a ripple of laughter in the courtroom.

"We all wish to thank you for your enlightened views, Mr. Russell," the Defender said and slowly walked toward his table. With his back toward Russell he then asked: "How many times were you married, Mr. Russell?"

"Objection," the Prosecutor protested, "that is irrelevant to the testimony of the witness."

"It is not irrelevant to the witness's credibility," the Defender replied.

"Objection overruled."

Russell cleared his throat. "Four times."

"Four times," the Defender repeated. "You wrote a book on marriage, didn't you?"

"Yes, I did," Russell answered.

"And one on education?"

"Yes."

"In fact the subject of education was very important to you, was it not?"

"Yes, it was."

"Is it correct to assume, then, Mr. Russell, that you strongly opposed religious education?"

"That is correct."

"And that, in your opinion, an education without God leads to a happier, more fulfilled life?"

"Absolutely," Russell answered.

"Naturally you applied that conviction to the education of your own children."

"I certainly did."

"No more questions," the Defender said. "I would like to call one of my own witnesses now, your honor."

The judge looked at the Prosecutor, who didn't object. "You are excused," the judge said to Russell.

Russell left the stand. The Defender, bent over his notes, waited until Russell had taken his seat in the back of the courtroom and then said: "I call to the stand Katharine Tait."

Katharine Tait, a middle-aged woman with horn-rimmed glasses, took the stand.

"Mrs. Tait," the Defender began, "your maiden name was Katharine Russell, was it not?"

"Yes," Mrs. Tait answered.

"And you are the daughter of Bertrand Russell?"

Mrs. Tait nodded.

"Would you tell us how your father's philosophy affected your own life, especially your own religious views?"

"My father was a great man," Mrs. Tait began, "he won the Nobel prize, you know. He had a mind as sharp as a razor and quick as a steel trap. He was full of zest for life, cheerful and kind. In whatever he did he had mankind in mind; he wanted to improve the lot of mankind."

The Defender grew impatient. "Certainly, Mrs. Tait, but what about the effect of his philosophy on you?"

Mrs. Tait looked down, concentrating, and then continued: "As children we were taught that we need not be afraid of anything. We could always speak to our parents about anything. It was an education to be rational and, of course, without any need for God."

120

Mrs. Tait hesitated and looked at her father.

"Would you tell us about your views on religion as an adult?" the Defender asked.

"I got married and had five children. My husband didn't believe in God either. But I was unhappy. I found myself in a small, miserable apartment in Washington with small children and I couldn't handle it. I couldn't make sense of my own existence. My father's solution—reason, progress, unselfishness—which I had heard all my life, didn't seem to work, it only filled me with despair."

"So I started going to church and later I convinced my husband to join me. What I heard there helped make sense out of everything. This was an Episcopalian church and it seemed that the Episcopalians had listened to criticism like my father's a long time ago and dropped the follies of the past; it was no longer the faith my father delighted in ridiculing. I realized, of course, that there were still weaknesses in the Christian argument; much of what my father said was true. Perhaps Christianity does not use watertight logic, but it certainly saved my sanity.

"My husband and I went to the theological seminary for three years and we became missionaries in Uganda. But things didn't work out for us, we stayed only two years. Then my husband had a few posts as minister of congregations on the East Coast, but during that time our marriage broke up."

The Defender, putting his hands on his hips, turned toward the Prosecutor. "And that is the effect of the philosophy of your great Bertrand Russell. Your witness."

The Prosecutor tapped his fingers on the table. "But religion didn't save your marriage either, did it?"

Mrs. Tait shook her head slowly.

"No more questions."

Mrs. Tait was excused.

"Are we entitled to say," the Prosecutor said, leaning

back in his chair, "that, because of one example, religion is indispensable to the happiness of mankind?"

"One and many other examples," the Defender replied.

"That doesn't prove anything," the Prosecutor countered. "I could bring witnesses who are deliriously happy without practicing a religion or without even believing in God. You could bring more witnesses who would state that they are happy because of their religion. It wouldn't get us anywhere. It depends far too much on the psychological make-up of the person."

The Prosecutor got out of his chair. "But I am far more concerned about your allegation that religion is necessary to make a person moral. That is a view straight out of the dark ages."

The Defender now stood up too, face to face with his opponent. "There is no doubt in my mind that the moral decay and the rising crime rate in our society today is directly linked to the reduced influence of religion. Our youth no longer gets the spiritual guidance it needs . . . "

"Poppycock," the Prosecutor shouted, "throughout the ages, from the Greek to the Romans to the middle ages every generation has complained about the lack of moral values in their youth."

"Gentlemen," the judge intervened, "this isn't getting us anywhere. I suggest we leave this subject. Call your next witness, Mr. Prosecutor."

Both of them sat down. The Prosecutor grabbed his notes and said: "I call to the stand Andrew Dickson White."

White appeared from the center of the courtroom. He passed by me nodding politely.

"Mr. White," the Prosecutor said, "I would like you to tell this court what you have found in your research into the history of Christianity."

"It's not a very pleasant story," White hesitated.

122

"I think we need to hear it," the Prosecutor insisted.

White began: "There is no doubt that Christianity has retarded the progress of mankind greatly. In many areas some of the ancient peoples, especially the Greeks, had made great progress. Take meteorology, for example. Plato and Aristotle attempted to account for wind, rain, lightning and thunder on natural grounds. But as the Christian church rose to power, all scientific work stopped. Supported by the scriptures the belief was, as had been during the times of the Old Testament, that thunder, wind and rainstorms and lightning were caused either by evil spirits or the wrath of God. The cure for these phenomena was the ringing of churchbells, brandishing relics of saints, or exorcism. In 1437 pope Eugene IV even issued a bull ordering the inquisitors to use greater diligence against the agents of the Prince of Darkness, especially against those who have the power to produce bad weather.

"And this wasn't just confined to the Catholic church. Luther, for example, believed that a stone thrown into a certain pond in his native region would cause a dreadful storm because of the devils imprisoned there.

"This belief about occurrences in nature was dominant in Christianity until 1752 when Benjamin Franklin flew his kite and drew lightning, thus proving that it was a natural phenomenon. He then proposed that tall buildings should be protected by lightning rods, but this was opposed by many clergymen as impiety, until it became finally obvious that buildings without lightning rods, among them many churches, burned down far more frequently than buildings which had a lightning rod. A case in point is the church of San Nazaro at Brescia. The Republic of Venice had refused to install a lightning rod even though more than 200,000 pounds of gunpowder were stored in it. In 1767 the church was struck by lightning, the powder exploded, one sixth of the entire city was destroyed and 3000 people were killed.

"And then there is, of course, the more famous case of astronomy. The belief of the church was that the earth was the center of everything. Copernicus proposed a concrete theory which put the sun at the center and the earth rotating around it. For 30 years he hesitated to publish his theory because he knew it would be dangerous. When he finally decided to write a book, his publisher put a disclaimer in it, saying that it was only a hypothesis. Copernicus saw the first copy the day he died in 1543.

"The publisher's disclaimer served the book well. The church took little notice of it for more than 70 years, though it became known in scientific circles. Giordano Bruno, who advocated similar theories, was burned alive by the inquisition in 1600.

"In 1615 Galileo proved Copernicus' theory with the telescope and a furor broke loose immediately. Galileo was brought before the inquisition and he had to promise not to publish anything advocating this theory.

"But Galileo did not give up. He published his famous *Dialogo*, the 'Dialogues Concerning the Two World Systems' in 1632. In this book three men discuss the opposing theories, so that Galileo himself did not need to make a statement and thus break his promise. But it didn't help him. He was thrown into prison at age 70 and forced to recant by Pope Urban VIII.

"The church did not reverse its position on the Copernican theory until 1822 and condemnation of the Copernican system was, again, not limited to the Catholic church. Martin Luther also said about Copernicus: 'This fool wishes to reverse the entire science of astronomy; but sacred scripture tells us that Joshua commanded the sun to stand still, and not the earth'. Calvin asked: 'Who will venture to place the authority of Copernicus above that of the Holy Spirit?'

124

"The same kind of opposition took place in biology. When Linnaeus discovered that plants have sexual systems, his writings were immediately banned. Buffon, the great genius of natural history, was forced to recant publicly. And when Alfred Russel Wallace and Charles Darwin jointly announced their theories of evolution in 1859, it was like a plough going through an anthill. Denunciations and sermons came flying at them from all sides.

"The most significant attack was that by Bishop Wilberforce of Oxford. He stated that the principle of natural selection was absolutely imcompatible with the word of God, that it contradicted the revealed relations of creation to its creator and that it was a dishonoring view of nature. The highpoint came at the meeting of the British Association for the Advancement of Science in 1860. Bishop Wilberforce had decided that this gathering presented the opportunity to quash the dangerous new evolutionary theory. In his speech he congratulated himself on not being a descendant from a monkey. T. H. Huxley then stood up and gave the famous answer, a devastating moment for those in Wilberforce's camp: 'If the question is put to me, would I rather have a miserable ape for a grandfather or a man highly endowed by nature and possessed of great means of influence, yet who employs these faculties and that influence for the mere purpose of introducing ridicule into a grave scientific discussion, I unhesitatingly affirm my preference for the ape'."

The courtroom broke into laughter and applause. White paused for a while before he continued.

"But the opposition of the church in the field of medicine is more serious. Greek medicine had been brought out of superstition by Hippocrates, but it reverted right back into superstition with the advent of Christianity. The church taught that diseases were caused either by possession of the devil or by God as a punishment for sins or trial of the spirit. The body was considered the temple of the Holy Spirit and for this reason progress in anatomy was at a complete standstill for more than a thousand years. Surgery was considered dishonorable and physicians who operated on the body were excommunicated. The church went even further than that. Any cure by natural means was considered irreligious; the proper way to cure a sick person was by supernatural means: relics, holy water and exorcism.

"The resistance to vaccination is a particularly sad example. Vaccination was discovered in 1796 by Edward Jenner. Jenner was attacked as irreligious and an Anti-Vaccination Society was formed in Boston. As late as 1885 religious prejudice toward vaccination among Catholics in Montreal was still so strong that they refused to be vaccinated during an outbreak of smallpox. The Protestant population, who had no longer any such prejudice, escaped the smallpox almost entirely, but among Catholics it became so serious that they had to be quarantined. The Board of Health ordered compulsory vaccination, but the Catholic clergy urged their flocks to take up arms rather than to submit to vaccination. The death toll among Catholics was enormous.

"Equally disturbing is the case of anesthetics. First advocated for obstetric use by James Young Simpson in Scotland, his idea met with a storm of opposition. From pulpit to pulpit Simpson's use of chloroform for difficult childbirths was denounced as impious and contrary to holy writ; texts were cited declaring that the use of chloroform was to 'avoid the primeval curse on woman'.

"Simpson wrote pamphlet after pamphlet to defend the use of chloroform, to no avail. But he finally found the right weapon when he wrote: 'My opponents forget the twenty-first chapter of Genesis; it is the record of the first surgical operation and the text proves that God, before he took the rib from Adam's side to create Eve, caused a deep sleep to fall upon Adam'."

Again there was laughter and White paused.

"The treatment of the insane is a grim chapter in medicine because of the power of the church. As early as the fifth century BC Hippocrates recognized that madness was a disease of the brain. By the third century AD it was known to medical science that the treatment for insanity must be gentle and kind. But the Christian church declared that madness was caused by possession of the devil and for 18 centuries the insane were 'cured' by exorcism, by beating, torturing and sometimes burning their bodies so that the devil would leave them. This persecution of the insane increased and became even more cruel with the advent of the inquisition, and both Luther and Calvin took part in it. The result was that there was a much larger percentage of insane people in the middle ages than there is today; with that kind of treatment temporary insanity became permanent and mild cases became violent.

"Such treatment also applied to hallucinations, a curious aspect to all of this. If a hallucination took a mild form, the person was treated with reverence and even elevated into sainthood, as the cases of St. Francis of Assisi and St. Catharine of Siena show. But if the hallucination was too strong this could backfire on the patient. A case here is Simon Marin, who in his insanity believed himself to be the Son of God. He was burned alive.

"It was not until the middle of the 18th century that the treatment of the insane became more scientific again. But even in my time exorcisms were still being performed."

And they are still being performed today, I thought to myself.

"Thank you, Mr. White," the prosecutor said.

The judge looked at the Defender, who had his elbow

propped on the table, supporting his chin with his hand. After a few seconds he said: "No questions."

White left the witness stand.

The Prosecutor got up and stood in front of the witness box, facing the Defender. "It is the contention of the defense," he said in a loud voice, "that the contributions of religion to society have been positive on the whole. After hearing Mr. White, there should be some doubt about this. But, I am afraid, there is more, much more. For example, we have not yet mentioned religious wars. Wars involving entire countries caused by religious differences—Christians against pagans, Protestants against Catholics."

The Prosecutor went to his table and picked up his notes.

"And the persecution of religious minority groups! In 1184 Pope Lucius III issued a decree against heretics and for 500 years every religious dissident was forced to live in fear and many religious sects were either driven out of Europe or exterminated. A vivid example is the case of the Stedinger, a small independent people in northern Germany who had been successful in rejecting subjection by both the feudal system and the clergy. In 1233 the Archbishop of Bremen asked Pope Gregory IX for help. The pope wrote to all the bishops: 'The Stedinger', he said, 'seduced by the devil, have abjured all the laws of God and man, slandered the church, insulted the holy sacraments, consulted witches to raise evil spirits, shed blood like water, took the lives of priests, and concocted an infernal scheme to propagate the worship of the devil, whom they adore under the name of Asmondi. The devil appears to them in different shapes, sometimes as a goose or a duck and at other times in the figure of a pale black-eyed youth, whose embrace fills their hearts with eternal hatred against the holy church of Christ. This devil presides at their sabbaths, when they all kiss him and dance around him'.

"As a result of this letter the bishops of Ratzebourg, Lubeck, Onsabrueck, Muenster and Minden took up arms together with six dukes and counts. An army of 40,000 men marched against the Stedinger and killed every man, woman and child.

"In 1252 torture for those suspected of heresy was officially approved by Pope Innocent IV and the inquisition became a power to be reckoned with all over Europe. An inquisitor's manual was written in 1376 and approved for official use by Pope Gregory XIII in 1578. This infamous document set the rules in the following way: A suspected heretic could be thrown into prison without accusation. His head was shaved and he was forced to take an oath before the crucifix that he would tell the truth. If he refused to take this oath he was condemned without further evidence.

"His legal council was not allowed to act in his interest or see him in private; his job was to convince the prisoner to admit his guilt.

"His family could testify against him but not for him. He was not allowed to know the identity of the witnesses against him. Unsupported testimony was acceptable; two hear-say witnesses equalled one eyewitness.

"His property was confiscated by the church. If he refused to admit his guilt he was tortured until he did. And if he was, in this way, found guilty of heresy, he was burned alive at the stake.

"The persecution of heretics was probably worst in Spain under the infamous inquisitor Torquemada, where, in a span of 18 years at least 10,000 people were burned alive and 100,000 were tortured.

"And we must not forget the persecution of the Jews, which started long before the Nazis. The council of Toledo in 633 declared that all the children of Jews should be taken away from them and put into monasteries. No Jew could be a witness against a Christian. In Spain, in 1492, the king signed an edict for the expulsion of the Jews. Of 235,000 Jews, 165,000 were forced to flee, 50,000 were baptized under force and 20,000 were killed.

"From 1290 on the Jews were banished from England for four centuries. They were expelled from France in 1182, losing all their property, from Vienna in 1196 and 1699, from Mecklenburg in 1225, from Breslau in 1226, from Frankfurt in 1241, from Brandenburg in 1243 and again in 1573. In Basle and Freyburg the Jews were suspected of having caused the black death. Wooden buildings were constructed, all the Jews of the town were driven into them and the buildings were burned down. And, again, the persecution of the Jews was not confined to Catholics; Protestants were often more vehement. Luther himself advocated the burning down of the synagogues.

"And we should also remember the crusades, an episode in history which most Christians think of as glorious. It was nothing of the kind; in truth it was one of the sorriest spectacles in the history of mankind.

"The first and largest crusade began in 1095 when Pope Urban II urged the people to conquer Palestine for Christianity. In 1096 three armies totalling more than 300,000 people left France and Germany and travelled through Hungary and Bulgaria toward Constantinople. The first army under Walter the Pennyless plundered their way through these countries, sacking towns and killing people. When they challenged the Turks, most were killed; the rest were disarmed and sent home.

"The second contingent under Peter the Hermit followed the path of the first. By now the people of Hungary and Bulgaria had enough of the plundering and killing and attacked. Of the 100,000 people, only 27,000 reached Constantinople. There most of the survivors were killed in a battle with the Turks, the rest were forced to become Moslems.

"The third army under a monk named Gottschalk

never even reached Constantinople; they were decimated in Hungary. So, of the first 300,000 crusaders only some 20,000 survived and not a single one reached Palestine.

"In 1097 leaders with cooler heads and more experience in soldiering recruited a second army of 300,000 people. Under the banner of Godfrey of Boullion, the Count of Toulouse and the brother of the king of France they reached Antioch relatively unharmed. There they lay siege to the city for more than a year and finally, losing most of their own people, sacked the city and killed the inhabitants. In 1099, more than two years after they had started out, they conquered Jerusalem with an army that was down to some 20,000 people.

"During the subsequent years Palestine was repeatedly lost again. There were seven more crusades, smaller than the first but equally disastrous. The strangest and saddest of these crusades was the children's crusade in 1213 where, by the belief that no harm could come to children, thousands—by some accounts 30,000 children—left for Palestine. Most of them died in shipwrecks, some were put to the sword, some were sold into slavery.

"During the eight crusades a total of at least 2 million men, women and children lost their lives!"

The Prosecutor stopped, went to his table and picked up different notes.

"And, lastly, the witchhunts. To most Christians today this is a quaint and amusing story, made fun of at Halloween. To a large number of people in the middle ages it was gruesome reality.

"The witch mania started with the bull of Pope Innocent VIII in 1485 in which he called the nations of Europe to the rescue of the church and described the horrors that had reached his ears: how witches had intercourse with the devil, how, by their sorceries they affected both man and beast, how they destroyed the births of women and the increase in cattle, how they blasted the corn, the grapes and

131

the fruits of the trees. He appointed inquisitors in every country and gave them apostolic power to convict and punish.

"The inquisitors set to work immediately. A suspected witch was tortured until she confessed and then was burned. Sometimes men and children suffered the same fate.

"No one was safe from this madness; anyone who had a grudge against someone else could accuse that person of sorcery and testify against him or her. Rapid incarceration and torture would follow and more often than not the accused person was burned or hanged. Even clergymen and judges occasionally became the victims. We have the detailed minutes of the trial of a Dietrich Flade, who was the chief judge of the Electoral Court in Triers, Germany. For a time he went along with the madness, but then he realized the unfairness of a confession in the torture chamber and refused to convict witches. He was arrested by the authority of the Archbishop and charged with having sold himself to Satan. He was tortured, confessed, and in 1589 he was strangled and burnt.

"Luther and Calvin, and even the Church of England, joined in the witchhunt. Matthew Hopkins called himself Witch-Finder General and pursued his trade with exuberance. At Bamberg, Germany, executions for witchcraft were at a rate of 100 annually. At Wuerzburg 257 burnings are recorded between 1627 and 1629. Among them we find a wife with two little sons, three boys of twelve, a girl of fifteen and one of nine. In France, during the reign of Henri III 30,000 women were burned as witches.

"In Scotland during Queen Mary's time some 17,000 witches were hanged or burned. In England, between 1600 and 1680 the number was 40,000. Between the appearance of the witch-hunt bull in 1485 and the last witch trial in

Salem, Massachusetts in 1692 more than half a million women were burned alive at the stake!''

The Prosecutor's voice had become louder and the last sentence he roared into the courtroom, pounding his fist on the table in front of him. ''During the time when the Christian religion reached its peak of influence, Europe was a hell-hole!''

The Prosecutor sat down.

The Defender stood up slowly, came over toward me in the jury box and then faced the Prosecutor. ''Why bring this up now? It all happened in the distant past. It is not relevant to Christianity today. Nobody is burning any witches any more.''

The Defender took a few tentative steps across the courtroom. ''And we cannot say that these attrocities were caused by the belief in God. People have been persecuting and killing each other for many different reasons, religion is just one of them. Take the killings under the communist regimes, for example. The number of people killed there far exceeds the numbers mentioned here, they even exceed the deathtoll of World War II. Yet few people today are particularly upset about that far more recent incident in history.''

The Defender now stood in front of the Prosecutor's table. ''But what galls me is that you completely ignore the tremendous amount of good Christianity has done. The selfless dedication of the clergy, the help given to the poor, sick and starving and the consolation to the dying. The schools and universities it has built to bring education into even the remotest corners of the world. Surely that outweighs what is merely human folly.''

''It is not human folly I object to,'' the Prosecutor said, ''but human folly—committed in the name of God!''

Epilogue

I found the Prosecutor in the small garden restaurant attached to the courthouse.

"May I bother you with a few questions, sir?" I asked.

The Prosecutor, somewhat annoyed at the intrusion, motioned me to sit down.

"I am curious to know why you have chosen to attack religion."

"I am not attacking religion," he answered. "I have no quarrels with religious people. No matter how unbelievable their convictions are to me I have no wish to interfere. But if that religious person or an entire religious organization attempts to wield influence over people who do not share their convictions, then I object. Religion should remain private. Take for example the debate on abortion. Most people who are against abortion are undeniably motivated by their religious beliefs. Now I respect their convictions but, as we have seen these are beliefs, not proven facts and they should not be used to impose a law on the population as a whole."

The Prosecutor finished his coffee and then continued: "The same is true for teaching creationism in public schools. It stems from a religious belief, there is no proof for it and for this reason we should not force it on the public, nor must we allow any kind of censorship of textbooks or public school curricula from religious motivation. And I hope there will come a time when we will keep religion out of politics.''

"Are you referring to the 'Moral Majority'?'' I asked.

The Prosecutor was ready to leave. "Yes, but it is much more widespread than that. Once you have examined religion in an impartial way you realize how much undue influence it has, even in a progressive nation such as ours.''

He grabbed his briefcase, casually dropped a few coins onto the table and said good-bye.

I looked down at the table, at the few coins near the empty cup of coffee and suddenly realized that on every coin it said:

"IN GOD WE TRUST"

Bibliography

Chapter 1:
THE ORIGIN

Baxter, Batsell B.: *I Believe Because* . . . , Baker Book House, Grand Rapids, Michigan, 1971

Baxter, Edna: *The Beginning of Our Religion,* Judson Press, Valley Forge, Pennsylvania, 1968

Durant, Will: *The Mansions of Philosophy,* Simon and Schuster, New York, 1929 (later renamed *The Pleasures of Philosophy*)

Durant, Will: *The Story of Civilization,* vol. 1, Our Oriental Heritage, Simon and Schuster, New York, 1935

Frazer, James G.: *The Golden Bough,* Macmillan, New York, 1922, 1963

Freud, Sigmund: *Moses and Monotheism,* Alfred A. Knopf, New York, 1949

Gordon, Cyrus H.: *Before the Bible,* Harper & Row, New York, 1962

Hopkins, E. Washburn: *Origin and Evolution of Religion,* Yale University Press, New Haven, 1923

Ingersoll, Robert G.: *Some Mistakes of Moses,* Freethought Press, New York, 1879

Jaynes, Julian: *The Origin of Consciousness in the Breakdown of the Bicameral Mind,* Houghton Mifflin, Boston, 1976

Kenyon, Frederic: *Our Bible and the Ancient Manuscripts,* Eyre & Spottiswoode, London, 1895, 1939

King, Leonard W.: *Legends of Babylon and Egypt in Relation to Hebrew Tradition,* British Academy, London, 1918

McDowell, Josh: *Evidence that Demands a Verdict,* 1972 and: *More Evidence that Demands a Verdict,* 1975, Campus Crusade for Christ Inc., San Bernardino, Ca.

Mencken, H. L.: *Treatise on the Gods,* Alfred A. Knopf, New York, 1930, 1946

Paine, Thomas: *The Age of Reason,* 1793/95, (*The Life and Major Writings of Thomas Paine,* Citadel Press, Secaucus, New Jersey, 1948, 1975)

Potter, Charles F.: *The Story of Religion,* Simon and Schuster, New York, 1929

Smith, George: *The Chaldean Account of Genesis,* Scribner Armstrong, 1876

Smith, Homer: *Man and His Gods,* Little Brown & Co., Boston, 1952

Smyth, J. Paterson: *How We Got the Bible,* James Pott & Co., 1899

Whitehead, Alfred N.: *Religion in the Making,* Macmillan, New York, 1930

Zimmern, Heinrich: *The Babylonian and the Hebrew Genesis,* David Nutt, London 1901 (translated from German)

Chapter 2:
THE PROOF

Adler, Mortimer: *How to Think about God,* Macmillan, New York, 1980

Barnes, Jonathan: *The Onthological Argument,* Macmillan, Edinburgh, 1972

Burill, Donald R. (ed.): *The Cosmological Arguments,* Doubleday Anchor Books, New York, 1967

Durant, Will: *The Pleasures of Philosophy* (originally: *The Mansions of Philosophy*), Simon and Schuster, New York, 1929, 1953

Friedrich, Carl J. (ed.): *The Philosophy of Kant,* Modern Library, New York, 1949

Hick, John H. (ed.): *The Existence of God,* Macmillan, New York, 1964

Hick, John H. and McGill, Arthur C. (ed.): *The Many-Faced Argument,* Macmillan, New York, 1967

Hume, David: *Dialogues Concerning Natural Religion,* 1779 (Hume on Religion, Meridian Books, The World Publishing Co., Cleveland, 1964)

Kaufmann, Walter: *The Faith of a Heretic,* McGraw-Hill, New York, 1959

Kueng, Hans: *Does God Exist? (Existiert Gott?),* Doubleday, New York, 1980

Matson, Wallace: *The Existence of God,* Cornell University Press, Ithaca, New York, 1965

Mossner, Ernest C.: *The Forgotten Hume,* Columbia University Press, New York, 1943

Rigg, J. M.: *St. Anselm of Canterbury,* Methuen & Co., London, 1896

Rowe, William L.: *The Cosmological Argument,* Princeton University Press, Princeton, 1975

Chapter 3:
THE UNIVERSE

Bronowski, Jacob: *The Ascent of Man,* Little Brown & Co., Boston, 1973

Burchfield, Joe D.: *Lord Kelvin and the Age of the Earth,* Science History Publications, Macmillan, London, 1975

Dukas, Helen and Hoffman, Banesh: *Albert Einstein, the Human Side,* Princeton University Press, Princeton, 1979

Eccles, John: *The Understanding of the Brain,* McGraw-Hill, New York, 1973

Einstein, Albert: *Mein Weltbild, 1934 (The World as I See It,* Citadel Press, Secaucus, N.J.)

Einstein, Albert: *Out of My Later Years,* Philosophical Library, New York, 1950

Einstein, Albert: *Ideas and Opinions,* Bonanza Books, New York, 1954

Ferris, Timothy: *The Red Limit,* William Morrow, New York, 1977

Folsom, Claire: *The Origin of Life,* W. H. Freeman & Co., San Francisco, 1979

Frankel, Edward: *DNA, Ladder of Life,* McGraw-Hill, New York, 1964

French, A. P. (ed.): *Einstein, A Centenary Volume,* Harvard University Press, Cambridge, Mass., 1979

Gamow, George: *The Creation of the Universe,* Viking Press, New York, 1952

Goldsmith, Richard: *The Material Basis of Evolution,* Yale University Press, 1940

Hayward, Alan: *God Is,* Thomas Nelson, Nashville, 1978

Hoffman, Banesh and Dukas, Helen: *Albert Einstein, Creator and Rebel,* Viking Press, New York, 1972

Hoyle, Fred: *The Nature of the Universe,* Harper and Brothers, New York, 1952

Hoyle, Fred: *Astronomy,* Crescent Books, 1957

Ingersoll, Robert: *Some Mistakes of Moses,* Freethought Press, New York, 1879

Jastrow, Robert: *Red Giants and White Dwarfs,* Harper & Row, New York, 1971

Jastrow, Robert: *Until the Sun Dies,* W. W. Morton & Co., New York, 1977

Jastrow, Robert: *God and the Astronomers,* W. W. Norton & Co., New York, 1978

Leakey, Richard and Lewin, Roger: *Origins,* E. P. Dutton, New York, 1977

Leakey, Richard: *People of the Lake,* Anchor Press/ Doubleday, Garden City, N. Y., 1978

Macbeth, Norman: *Darwin Retried,* Gambit, Boston, 1971

Morris, Henry M.: *The Troubled Waters of Evolution,* Creation-Life Publishers, San Diego, 1977

Morris, Henry M.: *The Scientific Case for Creation,* Creation-Life Publishers, San Diego, 1977

Murdin, Paul and Leslie: *The New Astronomy,* Thomas Crowell, New York, 1978

Oparin, A. I.: *Origin of Life,* Macmillan, 1938, Dover Publications, 1953

Ponnamperuna, Cyril: *The Origins of Life,* Dutton, New York, 1972

Restak, Richard M.: *The Brain,* Warner Books, New York, 1975

Rose, Steven: *The Conscious Brain,* Vintage Books, New York, 1976

Rush, J. H.: *The Dawn of Life,* Hanover House, Garden City, N. J., 1957

Sabine, Paul E.: *Atoms, Men and God,* Philosophical Library, New York, 1953

Sagan, Carl: *The Dragons of Eden,* Random House, New York, 1977

Sagan, Carl: *Cosmos,* Random House, New York, 1980

Shipman, Harry: *Black Holes, Quasars and the Universe,* Houghton Mifflin, Boston, 1976

Wooldridge, Dean: *The Machinery of Life,* McGraw-Hill, New York, 1966

Chapter 4:
MIRACLES

Hume, David: *Enquiry Concerning Human Understanding,* 1748, (Hume on Religion, Meridian Books, The World Publishing Co., Cleveland, 1964)

Lewis, C. S.: *Miracles,* 1947, Collins Fount Paperbacks, Glasgow

Loftus, Elizabeth: *Memory,* Addison-Wesley, Reading, Mass., 1980

Loftus, Elizabeth: *Eyewitness Testimony,* Harvard University Press, Cambridge, Mass., 1979

Mensching, Gustav: *Das Wunder im Aberglauben und Glauben der Voelker,* E. J. Brill, Leiden, 1957

Nolen, William A.: *Healing, A Doctor in Search of a Miracle,* Random House, New York, 1974

White, Andrew D.: *The Warfare of Science with Theology in Christendom, 1896,* George Braziller, New York, 1955

Chapter 5:
JESUS CHRIST

Augstein, Rudolf: *Jesus Menschensohn,* 1972, *(Jesus, Son of Man,* Urizen Books, New York, 1977)

Besant, Annie: *The Freethinker's Text-Book, part 2, Christianity,* reprint Arno Press, New York, 1972

Burrows, Millar: *The Dead-Sea Scrolls,* Viking Press, New York, 1955

Carmichael, Joel: *The Death of Jesus,* Macmillan, New York, 1962

Cross, Colin: *Who Was Jesus?,* Atheneum, New York, 1970

Dupont-Sommer, Andre: *The Essene Writings from Qumran,* World Publishing Co., Cleveland, 1967

Durant, Will: *The Story of Civilization, Cesar and Christ,* Simon and Schuster, New York, 1944

Grant, Michael: *Jesus, An Historian's Review of the Gospels,* Charles Scribner's Sons, New York, 1977

Langfeldt, Gabriel: *Albert Schweitzer,* George Braziller, New York, 1960, translated from Norwegian

LaSor, William: *The Dead Sea Scrolls and the New Testament,* William B. Eerdmans, Grand Rapids, Mich., 1972

McDowell, Josh: *More than a Carpenter,* Living Books, Wheaton, Ill., 1980

Oursler, Fulton: *The Greatest Story Ever Told,* Doubleday, Garden City, New York, 1949

Pagels, Elaine: *The Gnostic Gospels,* Random House Vintage Books, New York, 1979

Paine, Thomas: *The Age of Reason,* 1793, 1795, *(The Life and Writings of Thomas Paine,* Citadel Press, Secaucus, N. J., 1948, 1974)

Renan, Ernest: *Vie du Jesus,* 1863

Schweitzer, Albert: *Von Reimarus zu Wrede,* 1906. Second edition called *Die Geschichte der Leben Jesu Forschung,* 1913, (English translation of first edition: *The Quest of the Historical Jesus,* Macmillan, New York, 1950)

Schweitzer, Albert: *The Psychiatric Study of Jesus,* (translation), Beacon Press, Boston, 1948

Schweitzer, Albert: *The Mystery of the Kingdom of God,* (translation), Schocken Books, New York, 1964

Schweitzer, Albert: *Aus meinem Leben und Denken,* 1933. *(Out of my Life and Thought,* Henry Holt & Co., New York, 1949)

Seaver, George: *Albert Schweitzer,* Harper Bros., New York, 1947, revised edition 1955

Sheen, Fulton: *Life of Christ,* McGraw-Hill, New York, 1958

Trotter, F. Thomas (ed.): *Jesus and the Historian,* Westminster Press, Philadelphia, 1968

Chapter 6:
RELIGION

Mackay, Charles: *Extraordinary Popular Delusions and the Madness of Crowds,* 1841 (Farrar, Strauss & Giroux, New York, 1932)

Mill, John S.: *Nature and the Utility of Religion,* Longmans, Green & Co., London, 1874

Russell, Bertrand: *Why I Am Not a Christian,* Allen-Unwin, 1927 (Simon & Schuster, New York, 1957)

Summers, Montague: *Malleus Maleficarum,* John Rodker, London, 1927

Tait, Katharine: *My Father Bertrand Russell,* Harcourt Brace Jovanovich, New York, 1975

White, Andrew D.: *The Warfare of Science with Theology in Christendom,* 1896 (George Braziller, New York, 1955)